Personal Development and Work Experience Guide

Personal, Learning and Thinking Skills for the 21st Century

Edited by
John Mainstone and Ken Reynolds

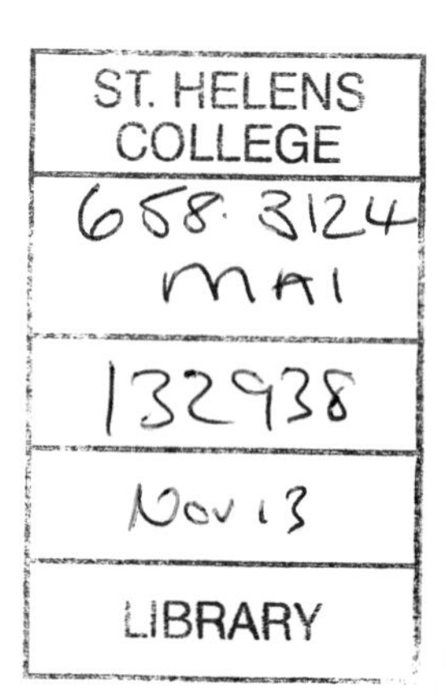

Personal Development and Work Experience Guide

This 7th edition published in 2013 by Cambridge Occupational Analysts Ltd
Sparham, Norwich, NR9 5PR

Editorial and Publishing Team

Editors John Mainstone and Ken Reynolds
Cover Design Made by PFD
Design and typesetting Simon Foster and Paul Rankin
Illustrations Diana Mainstone

British Library Cataloguing in Publication Data
A catalogue record for this book is available from the British Library.

ISBN 978-1-906711-18-4

Typeset by Cambridge Occupational Analysts Ltd, Sparham, Norwich NR9 5PR
Printed and bound in Great Britain by Clays Ltd, Bungay, Suffolk NR35 1ED

Disclaimer

While every effort has been made to ensure that all information in this book is up-to-date and accurate, and that all organisations listed are bona fide providers of opportunities for young people to develop their personal, learning and thinking skills, inclusion should not necessarily be assumed to be a recommendation. The authors do not accept any liability for errors, omissions or apparently misleading statements, nor for any loss, illness, injury or inconvenience resulting from the use of the information supplied. Readers must research all options with extreme thoroughness and reach their own judgment regarding the most suitable.

Contents

Introduction 2

Personal Development Opportunities 5

- Miscellaneous Projects - Overseas 6
- Community Projects in the UK 31
- Treks/Expeditions and Activity Holidays 36
- Work Experience 51
- Business and Journalism Skills 54
- Science, Engineering and Medicine 58
- Sports Related 63
- Language Skills 70
- Drama and Music 76
- Art and Design 80
- Cookery Skills 83

Important Information and Advice 89

- Fundraising 90
- Managing Risk 93
- Finding a Focus 96
- Am I Ready for a Trip Abroad? 98
- Further Information 104
- Suggested Reading List 107

Easter Revision Courses 109

Taster Courses 115

Indexes 133

- Subject Index 134
- Geographical Index 136
- Index of Taster Course Subjects 138
- Organisation Index 140

Introduction

This book is about how you can develop your abilities in ways that will help you succeed in your future career. It is aimed primarily at young people aged around 16 to 18. We envisage that most readers will be working towards AS/A levels, Highers or equivalent and will be in Year 12 or Scottish Year 5 (Y12/S5) at school or college. You may be starting to research possible courses of higher education, perhaps contemplating a Gap Year before going to university, and wondering what on earth you'll be able to write in your application that will have admissions tutors queuing up to recruit such an admirable student!

Our goal is to present you with a series of suggestions and exercises that will give you an idea of the many opportunities available and an understanding of how best to match these opportunities to your own needs.

Should you wish to improve your grades by re-taking examinations or by seeking extra tuition for your current studies, we list colleges offering this type of provision. We also give details of Taster courses provided by many universities and colleges which give you the chance to experience something of the academic and social life of an undergraduate student before you make a formal application.

Key Skills

Whatever you decide to do, try to look beyond the admittedly important elements of fun and excitement to think about whether your chosen activities will help develop the key skills needed for success in education, training, work and life in general.

The six key skills are:

- Application of number
- Communication - Written and Oral
- Improving your own learning and performance
- Information and communication technology
- Problem solving
- Teamwork/Working with others

These skills are relevant for everyone, from the youngest pupils in school to the most senior executives in large organisations. With the help of this book, not to mention time spent analysing your needs and exploring appropriate options, you should be able to improve the quality of your learning and performance by acquiring the ability to apply key skills in different contexts.

You should already have some knowledge of key skills, perhaps linked with a work experience programme in your school or college, together with curriculum enrichment activities. Key skills are also developed in the workplace and as part of university degree programmes. Not least, the achievement of key skills is recognised in the UCAS tariff for admission to higher education courses.

Try to identify skills you don't feel that you currently possess, or would like to reinforce, then think about how you could become involved in activities to help you develop those skills.

If you can provide examples from your own experience to illustrate the key skills, you will find that you have much of the material needed to complete the Personal Statement section of your university application. For more information on this, see our companion volume ***60 Successful Personal Statements for University Application*** edited by Guy and Gavin Nobes.

By tackling some of the projects outlined in this book, you could learn to lead with respect, to plan with safety and to participate with enthusiasm.

Once you feel motivated to develop your personal, learning and thinking skills, spend some time exploring the websites of the organisations listed on the following pages. The sheer number of agencies can be bewildering, so we have grouped them under headings to help you become aware of the range of opportunities available and decide what sort of activity best meets your needs. Please note, however, that many organisations offer such a variety of opportunities that they could easily be placed under several headings.

You can spend your time in the UK or overseas; you may be paid or you may have to pay a considerable sum in order to participate; you may choose a course of study or you may go on an expedition. Or maybe you've simply been stuck in the classroom for too long and need to get out in the fresh air and discover the delights of the great outdoors. It could be environmental work, sports coaching or some physically demanding adventure. The choice is yours.

Personal Development Opportunities

Miscellaneous Projects - Overseas

Organisations listed here may be broadly based or may specialise in one particular type of project. Some activities may be paid, some unpaid, while some are predominantly focused on academic study. Typical offerings might include Volunteering (Community Development, Construction, Conservation, Teaching), Internships (Media, Marketing, Health, Tourism, Sports Coaching), Tours (Cultural, Ecological, Humanitarian) and Jobs (all over the world). We have also listed under this heading some associations - such as the Year Out Group - acting as an umbrella group for several separate providers.

Africa and Asia Venture 18-25

AV, as it is generally known, recruits 18-25-year-olds, who want to combine four to five months of travel, safaris, adventure, friendship and fun in a year out with teaching or coaching sports, working with local communities or conservation work. You would normally start with a four-day in-country training course, then spend three to four months at your project, followed by one month of travel and safari. The latter could include seeing wildlife in African National Parks, visiting temples and palaces in Nepal, or adventure in Mexico. In Thailand, you would teach among the hill tribes for two months, followed by one month's project work, three weeks of travel/ adventure opportunities and a five-day open water diving course.

Countries: China, Ecuador, India, Kenya, Malawi, Mexico, Nepal, South Africa, Tanzania, Thailand, Uganda

Twitter: @AVentureUK

Web: **www.aventure.co.uk**

African Conservation Experience 17+

African Conservation Experience claims to be the most experienced organisation for conservation placements in Southern Africa. It can offer you the chance to work on game and nature reserves alongside conservationists, zoologists, wildlife vets and reserve managers. The organisation welcomes volunteers from all backgrounds, with no previous experience necessary, from the age of 17 upwards. Volunteer placements are from one to three months, and you can combine two or more projects in one trip. You could join a placement as part of a Gap Year, in a summer break from school or university, or as part of a career break or sabbatical.

Countries: Botswana, Mauritius, South Africa, Zimbabwe

Twitter: @AfricanConsExp

Web: **www.conservationafrica.net**

Agape Volunteers — 17+

Agape Volunteers are a registered charity and provide humanitarian aid and support to Africa through volunteering programmes. Choose from over six different programmes in the four distinct African regions of Kenya, South Africa, Ghana and Tanzania. Teach in a school, care for orphans, coach sport, help combat AIDS or volunteer as a medical student in one of their many placements. Volunteer for as long as you want, starting whenever you want and get the chance to experience frontline aid work. Agape also offer the chance to volunteer in the Himalayas.

Countries: Ghana, Kenya, South Africa, Tanzania

Twitter: @AgapeVolunteer

Web: **www.agape-volunteers.com**

Americamp — 18+

Americamp offers people around the world the chance to work at a summer camp in America either as a camp counsellor or in a support role that is 'behind the scenes'. Wages are the highest in the industry with a $1,500 starting salary even if you are only 19.

Countries: USA

Twitter: @AmeriCamp

Web: **www.americamp.co.uk**

Au Pair in America 18+

Working as an au pair in America can be a good way to discover the USA, as you can experience everyday life with a carefully selected American family and earn weekly pocket money by providing childcare as a nanny or babysitter. Whether you're looking for a year out or just want to work legally abroad, the exchange programmes on the Au Pair in America website give you free time to explore, study, travel and make new friends, together with professional support throughout your stay.

Countries: USA

Twitter: @aupairinamerica

Web: **www.aupairinamerica.com**

Azafady 18+

Azafady offer volunteers the opportunity to get involved in their projects in Madagascar through exciting and challenging programmes lasting from two to ten weeks. In their Pioneer Programme volunteers work on a variety of projects such as building and equipping schools, constructing wells, environmental education, and forest conservation. They provide two fortnight-long modules, in Lemur and Biodiversity Research and Community Conservation, which can be taken individually or combined. Their volunteering programmes are an excellent choice for anyone considering a career in development or conservation.

Countries: Madagascar

Twitter: @azafady

Web: **www.madagascar.co.uk**

Blue Ventures 17+

A not-for-profit organisation dedicated to facilitating projects and expeditions that enhance global marine conservation and research, Blue Ventures coordinates expeditions consisting of scientists and volunteers, working hand-in-hand with local biologists, governmental departments and communities, to carry out research, environmental awareness and conservation programmes at threatened marine habitats around the world.

Countries: Belize, Madagascar

Twitter: @BlueVentures

Web: **www.blueventures.org**

BUNAC 18+

BUNAC offers a range of working holidays, including a summer camp counselling programme in the USA and Canada, flexible work and travel programmes to Canada, the USA, Australia, New Zealand and South Africa, and volunteering/teaching placements. These are open to 18-year-olds and over in the UK, the USA and Ireland. Programmes last from five weeks to two years.

Countries: Australia, Canada, China, Ghana, Nepal, New Zealand, South Africa, USA

Twitter: @BUNAC_UK

Web: **www.bunac.org/uk/**

Camp America 18+

Each year over 7,500 young people take the opportunity to join Camp America and spend the summer in the USA, living and working either with children or 'behind the scenes' as support staff on an American Summer Camp. Following the end of your placement, you'll have up to two months to travel (in total your visa allows for up to four months' placement followed by one month of travel but most placements end well within four months).

Countries: USA

Twitter: @CampAmerica69

Web: **www.campamerica.co.uk**

Changing Worlds 17+

With a wide variety of paid and voluntary placements worldwide, Changing Worlds offers project types ranging from medical, sports coaching, teaching, conservation, orphanage, zoo work to farming placements.

Countries: Argentina, Australia, Brazil, China, Dubai, Germany, Ghana, Honduras, India, Kenya, Madagascar, New Zealand, Romania, South Africa, Tanzania, Thailand, Uganda

Twitter: @Changing_Worlds

Web: **www.changingworlds.co.uk**

Concordia 16-30

In addition to UK farm placements, Concordia offers an extensive international volunteer programme. Short-term projects bring together individuals from around the world to participate in two- to four-week projects in Western, Eastern and Central Europe, North America, North Africa, Japan, or in Africa, Asia and Latin America. Medium-term projects usually last between one and six months, although they occasionally last for a whole year.

Countries: Worldwide

Twitter: @ConcordiaVol

Web: **www.concordiavolunteers.org.uk**

Coral Cay Conservation 16+

Coral Cay Conservation (CCC) is a not-for-profit organisation at the cutting edge of ecotourism. It sends teams of volunteers to survey some of the world's most endangered coral reefs and tropical forests. Its mission is to protect these crucial environments by working closely with the local communities who depend on them for food and livelihood. CCC currently has coral reef expeditions in Tobago and the Philippines and forest expeditions in the Philippines and Papua New Guinea. The organisation is largely financed by volunteers, who pay to participate in an expedition for anything from one week upwards. Volunteers require no scientific background and are trained on-site in marine or terrestrial ecology and survey techniques.

Countries: Cambodia, Montserrat, Philippines

Twitter: @CoralCay

Web: **www.coralcay.org**

Ecoteer 18+

Ecoteer works by providing a site where volunteers can find work. By eliminating the middleman the cost of volunteering is greatly reduced giving more people the chance to volunteer abroad. All volunteering enquiries go straight to the projects so you can trust all the information you get is 100% accurate and up-to-date. Ecoteer offers cheap volunteer work and job opportunities at eco lodges, conservation, farm, teaching and humanitarian projects worldwide. It offers different types of placement such as ecotourism in Malaysia, a sea turtle conservation project in Costa Rica, humanitarian and teaching projects in Ecuador.

Countries: Worldwide

Twitter: @ecoteer

Web: **www.ecoteer.com**

Experiment in International Living 16+

Your community service as an EIL Volunteer for International Partnership (VIP) could be working with a rural development project, volunteering in a health clinic, working with children or teaching English. VIP offers individuals or groups the opportunity to volunteer abroad in over 14 countries. Most programmes include language training and homestays with families - an excellent way to meet people and learn about local culture.

Countries: Albania, Argentina, Brazil, Canada, Chile, China, Ecuador, Eire, France, Germany, Guatemala, Ghana, Italy, Japan, Korea, Malta, Mexico, Morocco, New Zealand, Nigeria, South Africa, Spain, Turkey, UK, USA

Web: **www.eiluk.org**

Frontier 17+

Frontier was established as a non-profit conservation and development non-governmental organisation dedicated to safeguarding biodiversity and ecosystem integrity and building sustainable livelihoods for marginalised communities in the world's poorest countries. With a long record of conserving biodiversity, discovering new species, building environmental awareness and developing sustainable livelihoods, Frontier offers 'hands-on' fieldwork, which benefits endangered tropical wildlife and their ecosystems and directly assists developing countries rich in biodiversity but poor in the capacity to manage natural resources.

Countries: Worldwide

Twitter: @FrontierGap

Web: **www.frontier.ac.uk**

Gapwork 17+

Whether it's skiing in the Rocky Mountains, volunteering in a South African safari park or tracking river dolphins in the Amazon that you want, you should find something suitable in the Gapwork activities section. Other sections include jobs, community development, sports and study abroad.

Twitter: @GapworkJobs

Web: **www.gapwork.com**

Global Choices 17+

Based in London, Global Choices offers programmes classified in five types: Working Holidays, Internships, Teaching Abroad, Volunteering and Courses. Destination countries include Greece, Spain, Ireland, USA, Australia, China, India, Canada, Argentina, Costa Rica and Brazil, in addition to the United Kingdom.

Countries: Argentina, Australia, Brazil, Canada, China, Costa Rica, Cyprus, Greece, India, New Zealand, Portugal, Spain, UK, USA

Twitter: @GlobalChoices

Web: **www.globalchoices.co.uk**

Global Volunteer Network 15-17, 18+

This network offers volunteer opportunities in community projects throughout the world, currently providing volunteer programmes through partner organisations across South America, Asia and Africa. Their vision is to connect people with communities in need, with a particular focus on vulnerable women and children. This is done by supporting the work of local community organisations in countries through the placement of international volunteers. Personal benefits include development of life skills, personal growth, friendship, increased self-confidence, and building independence.

Countries: Argentina, Cambodia, Costa Rica, Ecuador, Ethiopia, Ghana, Guatemala, Kenya, Nepal, New Zealand, Panama, Peru, Philippines, Rwanda, South Africa, Thailand, Uganda, Vietnam

Twitter: @GVNnFoundation

Web: **www.globalvolunteernetwork.org**

Global Volunteer Projects 17+

Offers a variety of placements and projects across the world including medical placements, teaching projects, HIV awareness projects, journalism placements, conservation projects and orphanage placements. You could find yourself working at a Ghanaian TV station, at an orphanage in Cambodia or helping to preserve endangered Sea Turtles on the Pacific coast of Mexico.

Countries: Cambodia, China, Ghana, India, Mexico, Romania, Tanzania

Web: **www.globalvolunteerprojects.org**

Greenforce 17+

Much of Greenforce's current activity is focused on conserving coral reefs. Widely known as the rainforests of the sea, the reefs are home to a massive diversity of species and are much more than just a pretty underwater garden for divers to enjoy. On land, the competition for living space and resources is pushing wildlife into ever shrinking zones. Another major part of the work that Greenforce does is to contribute to improving the lives of fragile and threatened communities, such as the Maasai in parts of Tanzania, and the Quichua Indians deep in the Amazon jungle.

Countries: Australia, Bahamas, Belize, Borneo, Botswana, China, Ecuador, Fiji, Galápagos Islands, Ghana, Guatemala, India, Namibia, Nepal, Peru, South Africa, Tanzania, Zambia, Zimbabwe

Web: **www.greenforce.org**

GVI Foundations 15-17

Global Vision International (GVI) provides support to international charities, non-profit and governmental agencies. GVI is a recognised leader in international volunteering and has sent over 10,000 volunteers overseas to aid critical environmental and humanitarian programmes. GVI works hand in hand with local communities, international and local charities and governmental organisations to ensure the long-term sustainability of all its programmes.

Countries: Costa Rica, Fiji, Greece, India, Kenya, Laos, Mexico, Nepal, Peru, Seychelles, South Africa, Spain, Thailand, USA

Twitter: @GVIFoundations

Web: **http://gvifoundations.co.uk**

Habitat for Humanity 18+

An international charity working to end poverty housing around the world, Habitat for Humanity works in some 3,000 communities in over 70 countries. You would normally spend around two weeks on location in a small community, actually building a house hand in hand with a partner family.

Countries: Worldwide

Twitter: @HabitatFHGB

Web: **www.habitatforhumanity.org.uk**

Help to Educate 18+

Help to Educate is a small registered charity that raises money to fund the education of child labourers in Nepal. It makes it possible to move children from dangerous working conditions and place them in a hostel where they can live and study. Most of the funds are raised by arranging for volunteers to teach in Nepal throughout the year. To teach in a Nepal school or help deprived children in a hostel can be a challenging, adventurous and worthwhile experience for people of any age and background.

Countries: Nepal

Web: **www.help2educate.org**

i to i Volunteering 17+

In the past 12 months, i-to-i volunteering has helped 5,000 people volunteer for projects in 23 countries. You can volunteer from all over the world from as little as one week up to several months. Volunteers engage with a local community in a unique way and experience part of another country not easily accessible to tourists. You can also be trained to Teach English as a Foreign Language (TEFL). Teaching English overseas is a perfect opportunity for any English speaker to explore the world.

Countries: Australia, Botswana, Brazil, Cambodia, China, Costa Rica, Ecuador, India, Indonesia, Kenya, Malaysia, Mozambique, Namibia, Nepal, Peru, South Africa, Sri Lanka, Swaziland, Tanzania, Thailand, Vietnam

Twitter: @itoiranger

Web: **www.i-to-i.com**

International Voluntary Service (IVS GB) 18+

A peace organisation working for the sustainable development of local and global communities throughout the world, IVS GB is the British contact for Service Civil International, a worldwide network of like-minded voluntary organisations promoting peace and justice through voluntary work. By taking part in an International Voluntary Project, you will be working and living alongside other volunteers from all over the world and contributing to local community development. There are hundreds of projects to choose from, including environmental conservation on beaches in Morocco, help at a centre for children with disabilities in Latvia, work with elderly people in mountain villages in Japan, a community theatre in the Czech Republic, and youth work in Russia.

Countries: Worldwide

Twitter: @IVSGB

Web: **www.ivsgb.org**

IST Plus 17+

With an IST Plus cultural exchange programme you can work, study, travel or teach in locations throughout the world. Work in the USA, teach in Thailand or China, travel around Australia and New Zealand and Singapore, or study a language anywhere in the world.

Countries: Australia, Cambodia, China, New Zealand, Singapore, Thailand, USA

Twitter: @ISTPlusWorld

Web: **www.istplus.com**

Kibbutz Volunteers 18-35

Living and working in a kibbutz community in Israel, carrying out the true principles of a socialistic society, having all work, property and profit equally shared by its members, can form the basis of an intriguing working holiday experience. A holiday with the possibility to meet, live and work with both Israeli youngsters and other kibbutz volunteers from countries and cultures far and near.

Countries: Israel

Twitter: @KIBBUTZwebsi

Web: **www.kibbutz.org.il/eng**

Lattitude Global Volunteering 17-25

Lattitude organises voluntary work overseas, and similar exchange voluntary opportunities for overseas nationals in the UK. Lattitude volunteers work alongside staff in such roles as foreign language assistants, assisting with general activities in schools, caring for the disadvantaged, or in outdoor education and conservation work. Whatever the nature of your placement, it will always be a challenge. You could be working in an environment different from anything you've ever experienced, so you need to adapt to your responsibilities with maturity. As well as making a real difference to the lives of others, you'll certainly learn a lot about yourself.

Countries: Argentina, Australia, Canada, China, Ecuador, Fiji, France, Ghana, India, Japan, Malawi, New Zealand, Poland, South Africa, Vanuatu, Vietnam

Twitter: @LattitudeUK

Web: **www.lattitude.org.uk**

Love Volunteers 15-17, 18+

Love Volunteers offers 'not-for-profit programme fees' for fun, rewarding, safe and affordable volunteering opportunities in developing countries around the world. Love Volunteers have a variety of programs available, whether you're planning a week helping a local community as you travel around a country, want to spend six months learning the local language or are putting your gap year to good use.

Countries: Albania, Cambodia, Cameroon, China, Costa Rica, Ecuador, Ethiopia, Ghana, Honduras, India, Kenya, Malawi, Mexico, Moldova, Mongolia, Morocco, Nepal, Palestine, Peru, Russia, Senegal, South Africa, Tanzania, Thailand, Uganda, Ukraine, Vietnam, Zambia

Twitter: @LoveVolunteer

Web: **www.lovevolunteers.org**

Outreach International 16+

This specialist organisation has a wide variety of projects, all of them small, grassroots initiatives working with communities where volunteer work can make a big difference. Placements last between one month and twelve months and could involve anything from working with children – in schools or orphanages – to helping out at an animal rescue centre. Other projects include rainforest and marine conservation, teaching English or art and craft, or medical-related projects, such as physiotherapy.

Countries: Cambodia, Costa Rica, Ecuador, Galápagos Islands, Kenya, Mexico, Nepal, Sri Lanka, Tanzania

Twitter: @Outreachint

Web: **www.outreachinternational.co.uk**

Oyster Worldwide 18+

Oyster Worldwide is a well regarded gap year travel and responsible travel specialist. It offers projects working with children and teaching English in Brazil, Chilean Patagonia, Kenya, Nepal, Romania and Tanzania. Pre-departure training is included, as well as appropriate language training on arrival. The company also has some paid work opportunities in hotels and ski resorts in the Canadian Rockies and Quebec.

Countries: Australia, Brazil, Cambodia, Canada, Chile, Costa Rica, France, India, Jordan, Kenya, Nepal, Romania, South Africa, Tanzania, Thailand, Zambia

Twitter: @OysterWorldwide

Web: **www.oysterworldwide.com**

Pacific Discovery 18-24

Pacific Discovery offers inspiring gap year, experiential and educational travel programmes to the most amazing places on earth. Its award-winning programmes blend meaningful and challenging travel, cultural immersion, personal and leadership development, outdoors and wilderness exploration, volunteer and community service projects, ethical travel and sustainability focus.

Countries: Australia, Cambodia, Ecuador, Galápagos Islands, Laos, Myanmar, Nepal, New Zealand, Peru, Thailand, Tibet, Vietnam

Twitter: @pacificdiscovry

Web: **www.pacificdiscovery.org**

PGL 18+

PGL provides children's adventure holidays at its 24 activity centres across the UK, France and Spain. Every year it recruits over 2,500 staff to instruct, inspire and look after its guests, with vacancies for watersports instructors, adventure activity instructors, group leaders, language speakers, administrators, and maintenance, catering and domestic staff. There are also ad hoc ski rep positions for the peak weeks of the winter operating season.

Countries: France, Spain, UK

Twitter: @pglstaff

Web: **www.pgl.co.uk/jobs**

PoD Volunteer 18+

PoD provides the opportunity for you to volunteer and make a difference in parts of the world that are rich in culture, variety and natural beauty but where there is poverty or disadvantage. You may be on your gap year or wanting to volunteer as part of a working holiday abroad for 1 week to 6 months. Volunteers are needed to help work with disadvantaged children, communities, animal and conservation projects.

Countries: Belize, Cambodia, Ghana, Nepal, Peru, South Africa, Thailand, Vietnam

Twitter: @podvolunteer

Web: **www.podvolunteer.org**

Project Trust 17-19

Based on the Isle of Coll, Project Trust specialises in 12- or 8-month volunteer placements giving you plenty of time to explore your new surroundings, whilst working in the local community. You can choose from over 20 different countries, spending a year living, working and travelling in Africa, Asia, Latin America or the Caribbean with a wide variety of work and a diverse range of cultures.

Countries: Bolivia, Botswana, Cambodia, Chile, China, Dominican Republic, Ghana, Guyana, Honduras, Hong Kong, India, Jamaica, Japan, Malawi, Malaysia, Namibia, Peru, Senegal, South Africa, Sri Lanka, Swaziland, Thailand, Uganda

Twitter: @ProjectTrustUK

Web: **www.projecttrust.org.uk**

Projects Abroad 16+

With a wide range of projects, including teaching, care, conservation, medicine & healthcare and journalism, Projects Abroad organises overseas voluntary work placements designed specifically for the communities where it works. The teaching projects focus on conversational English teaching and don't require TEFL qualifications. You could teach in Africa, Asia, Latin America or Eastern Europe, as part of a project in a school, university or orphanage. In journalism, you could work on a Chinese, Indian, Ghanaian, Mexican, Moldovan, Mongolian, Romanian or Sri Lankan newspaper or work at a radio station in Ghana, Senegal or Mexico, or even a TV station in Mongolia. A range of medical, conservation, animal care, business and sports internships are also available.

Countries: Worldwide

Twitter: @Proj_Abroad_UK

Web: **www.projects-abroad.co.uk**

Real Gap Experience 17+

Real Gap Experience is one of the leading independent Gap Year providers offering a comprehensive range of exciting volunteering, paid work, sports, adventure travel, language courses and career breaks in over 40 countries, from 2 weeks to 2 years. They can organise a complete gap year away unique to you (including flights and insurance) with a strong emphasis on security and safety. All their experienced advisers have taken their own gap years and will provide help and support to plan yours.

Countries: Worldwide

Twitter: @Real_Gap

Web: **www.realgap.co.uk**

Restless Development 18-28

If you are passionate about changing lives and want to make a difference to the community that you work with, you can volunteer to work for five to eleven months in India, Zambia, Uganda, Tanzania, South Africa or Nepal. You might find yourself helping vulnerable young people protect themselves against HIV, open a library or a youth centre, construct a smokeless stove or establish a recycling programme.

Countries: India, Nepal, Sierra Leone, South Africa, Tanzania, Uganda, UK, USA, Zambia, Zimbabwe

Twitter: @RestlessDev

Web: **www.restlessdevelopment.org**

The Conservation Volunteers — All ages

The Conservation Volunteers (TCV) have a successful history of environmental conservation volunteering throughout the UK and around the world. TCV holidays take place all year round in some of the world's finest landscapes. Living, laughing and cooking together, you'll be busy all over, all the time. TCV holidays don't just improve the environment - they're good for your health and could change your life.

Countries: Albania, Bulgaria, Cameroon, Estonia, France, Germany, Iceland, Italy, Japan, Lesotho, Portugal, Romania, Slovakia, South Africa, Spain, UK, USA

Twitter: @TCVtweets

Web: **www.tcv.org.uk**

Travellers Worldwide — 17+

Offering a variety of voluntary projects lasting from two weeks to a year, Travellers Worldwide seeks to help children, adults, animals and entire communities in less advantaged countries. The only qualifications you need are a spirit of adventure and a sense of humour.

Countries: Argentina, Australia, Brazil, Cambodia, China, Ecuador, Ghana, India, Kenya, Malaysia, Mauritius, Morocco, Nepal, New Zealand, Peru, South Africa, Sri Lanka, Thailand, USA, Zambia, Zimbabwe

Twitter: @TravellersWW

Web: **www.travellersworldwide.com**

Twin Work And Volunteer — All ages

Twin Work And Volunteer provides a wide range of programmes allowing people of all backgrounds and ages the opportunity to participate in community and conservation volunteering projects around the world as well as internships and paid work placements. They currently offer around 80 programmes in more than 20 countries. Some of their most popular internship and work programmes are in Spain, Norway, France and Australia. Conservation projects are in Ecuador, Galápagos Islands, South Africa, Thailand, Vietnam and New Zealand, and they also send many volunteers to community projects in Chile, Ghana, Mozambique, Tanzania, Swaziland, India and Nepal.

Countries: Worldwide

Twitter: @Work_Volunteer

Web: **www.workandvolunteer.com**

Visit Oz — 17-30

If you are considering a gap year in Australia before you go to university, after you have graduated or at any time before your 31st birthday, Visit Oz guarantees to find you a job on the land or in rural hospitality, as well as providing agricultural or hospitality training. You must have a Working Holiday Visa (or other Visa allowing work) and be prepared to get your hands dirty. Outback farm or station work can include working with horses, cattle and sheep, tractor and header driving, bulldozer work, fencing, mechanical work, and chainsaw work; horse work may be at stables, in trail riding centres, on Host Farms, with racehorses, polo ponies, camp draft horses, or on cattle properties doing bore running, yard work, and maintenance; agricultural bike work is with cattle and sheep. There are so many jobs that it is possible to find something to suit the skills of everybody.

Countries: Australia

Web: **www.visitoz.org**

Volunteer Action for Peace 18+

Volunteer Action for Peace (VAP) is a UK-based charity organisation which works towards creating and preserving international peace, justice and human solidarity for people and their communities. Through a range of working projects both in the United Kingdom and around the world, VAP provides volunteers with opportunities to work together with people from around the globe and in partnership with local groups to enhance and empower communities.

Countries: Worldwide

Twitter: @VAP_UK

Web: **www.vap.org.uk**

Volunteering India 18+

Volunteering India provides safe, affordable and meaningful volunteer programmes in India. They offer a variety of volunteer work, cultural exchange, internships, and gap years in India, where volunteers can choose to work in New Delhi, Palampur/Dharamsala and South India. You could work with orphans, in women empowerment, Health/HIV, teaching English, summer volunteer work or a street children volunteer programme.

Countries: India

Twitter: @indiavolunteer

Web: **www.volunteeringindia.com**

VSO 18+

VSO has programmes and volunteers in over 30 countries across Africa, Asia and the Pacific. It offers a Youth Volunteering programme for young people aged 18 to 25, although its main volunteers are aged from 20 to 75 and must have a formal qualification and relevant work experience. Regular postings are for two years and volunteers are provided with accommodation and a local level allowance as well as air fares and insurance.

Countries: Worldwide

Twitter: @VSOUK

Web: **www.vso.org.uk**

Winant Clayton Volunteers 18+

Winant Clayton has over 50 years' experience placing volunteers in community projects in the United States. You could work with children, the elderly, the homeless, adults with mental health problems and many more. Previous experience is valuable but not essential. You will get direct experience of being part of a local community project in the United States. The work will be challenging and you will discover skills, potential and strengths that you never knew you had.

Countries: USA

Twitter: @WinantClayton

Web: **www.winantclayton.org.uk**

Worldwide Volunteering 16+

Worldwide Volunteering (WWV) makes it easy for people of all ages to volunteer, by offering a 'search and match' database with over 2,400 volunteer organisations and 1.9 million placements throughout the UK and in 214 countries worldwide.

Twitter: @WWV_Volunteer

Web: **www.wwv.org.uk**

Year Out Group 17+

Formed in 1998 to promote the concept and benefits of well-structured year out programmes, to promote models of good practice and to help young people and their advisers in selecting suitable and worthwhile projects, Year Out Group is a not-for-profit association of UK-registered organisations that specialise in this field. All the member organisations are carefully vetted on joining and provide annual confirmation that they continue to abide by the Group's Code of Practice and Operating Guidelines.

Twitter: @YearOutGroupOrg

Web: **www.yearoutgroup.org**

Community Projects in the UK

In this section, you may be able to live at home and work on a local volunteer project, while some schemes insist that being away from home is an essential part of the gap year experience.

Community Service Volunteers 18-35

The UK's largest volunteering and training organisation, CSV provides hundreds of full-time volunteering opportunities across the UK that will equip you with life skills and enhance your CV or UCAS application. You will spend 6-12 months living away from home, supporting people in need and enabling them to develop or manage their own lives. As a CSV volunteer you will take on an important role that is valued by the community. You can use your skills and develop new ones, test yourself out in new situations, challenge your way of thinking, and make a genuine and positive impact on people's lives. CSV's placements are community-based, supporting a wide variety of people. You may be helping people with physical disabilities or learning difficulties, or supporting elderly people, children or young people.

Twitter: @CSV_UK

Web: **www.csv.org.uk**

CSV Heritage Camps 16-25

Experience the hidden history of some of Britain's oldest and most beautiful buildings. Cathedrals, abbeys, minsters, chapels and parish churches make up a huge part of Britain's architectural heritage and every year teams of young people from all over the world move in to help refresh and conserve these buildings. Cathedral Camps have been running week-long residential breaks at cathedrals and churches throughout the UK for over 30 years - there are on average 20 camps at different venues, running each year throughout July and August. Cathedral Camps is now run by the UK volunteering agency CSV (Community Service Volunteers), mentioned opposite.

Web: **http://cathedralcamps.org.uk**

Do-it All ages

The Do-it website is a volunteering database run by charity Youthnet. The search works on locations, just enter your postcode or town to find opportunities in your area and search through one million opportunities to volunteer and apply online. The majority of opportunities available come from local Volunteer Centres.

Web: **www.do-it.org.uk**

National Trust — All ages

If you don't want to travel too far but are still looking for a way to make a difference in conserving the environment and the UK's heritage, the National Trust could have something to offer. As a volunteer, you can learn new skills and meet new people while working right at the heart of beautiful buildings, gardens and landscapes. The Trust also runs around 450 Working Holidays every year throughout England, Wales and Northern Ireland, where you could be involved with anything from carrying out a conservation survey to herding goats, painting a lighthouse or planting trees.

Twitter: @nationaltrust

Web: **www.nationaltrust.org.uk/get-involved/volunteer/**

National Trust for Scotland — 16+

The National Trust for Scotland offers plenty of volunteering opportunities in the heritage sector. They also organise week long residential working holidays at NT Thistle Camps, where you can get involved in conserving the historic locations under its care. Campers can live and work in some of Scotland's most remarkable and remote places. Whilst Thistle camps are for over 18s, the trust also runs Trailblazer camps for 16- and 17-year-olds.

Twitter: @N_T_S

Web: **www.nts.org.uk/Volunteering**

Prince's Trust Volunteers — 14-30

The Prince's Trust helps young people overcome barriers and get their lives working. Through practical support including training, mentoring and financial assistance, the Trust helps 14-30-year-olds realise their potential and transform their lives. The main target groups are those who have struggled at school, been in care, been in trouble with the law, or are long-term unemployed. As a volunteer with the Trust, you could have a powerful influence on the success of its programmes, and on the young people they help.

Twitter: @PrincesTrust

Web: **www.princes-trust.org.uk**

Reach — Adult

Not aimed primarily at school or college leavers, Reach seeks to match the skills of experienced people to the needs of voluntary organisations. Reach recruits and supports people with managerial, technical and professional expertise and places them in part-time, unpaid roles in voluntary organisations that need their help. Volunteers are placed with organisations near where they live, anywhere in the UK.

Twitter: @ReachSkills

Web: **www.reachskills.org.uk**

vInspired 14-25

vInspired helps young people to discover the value of volunteering - for themselves and for others. It offers fun, easy-to-access opportunities that get young people excited about doing good things. Its online market-place and mobile apps link young people with interesting and varied opportunities with almost 2,000 charities across the country. Its innovative programmes – Do Something, Team v, v24/24, vInspired Cashpoint and National Citizen Service Summer of a Lifetime - provide structured support for young people to do good and gain new skills in their own ways. Whether young people have never volunteered before, or are veteran volunteers, whether they have an hour or a week to give, vInspired has a project or opportunity for them.

Twitter: @vinspired

Web: **www.vInspired.com**

Volunteering England All ages

Volunteering England is a part of the National Council for Voluntary Organisations, committed to supporting, enabling and celebrating volunteering in all its diversity. Their work links policy, research, innovation, good practice and programme management in the involvement of volunteers. They provide contact details of Volunteer Centres that can help individuals find volunteering opportunities in their local area.

Twitter: @NCVOvolunteers

Web: **www.volunteering.org.uk**

Treks/Expeditions and Activity Holidays

If you want to combine an adventure trek with an environmental, scientific or community project, you may find something suitable here. Expect to pay a substantial participation fee, for which you may have to raise sponsorship. Apart from being one of the best ways in which to fund your expedition, the experience of having to secure a considerable sum of money will help develop a range of skills before you even leave home! Expedition programmes give you the opportunity to develop many other important skills such as communication and time management. You'll be building confidence and self-esteem, in addition to learning to lead the expedition team and taking your turn to do so.

Adventure Jobs 16+

If you are looking for a job in adventure activity, travel, water sports or skiing, you may find something suitable here. The site lists vacancies for activity instructors, group leaders, centre managers, resort staff, chefs, nannies, receptionists, drivers and support staff, among many others.

Web: **www.adventurejobs.co.uk**

Australia Working Holiday 18-30

If you hold a valid UK passport and are aged between 18 and 30, you are eligible to apply for a Working Holiday Visa which will enable you to stay in Australia for up to 12 months, work with one employer for up to 6 months, study up to 4 months and leave and re-enter any number of times in the 12-month period. There is a huge variety of work on offer from bar work to fruit picking to working as a deck hand on a yacht.

Twitter: @australia

Web: **www.australia.com/workingholiday**

British Exploring 16+

British Exploring organises extreme adventure and conservation expeditions in remote, wild environments. You could find yourself monitoring climate change in the Arctic, measuring biodiversity in the jungle or investigating human impact on the environment in mountainous regions. The aim is always to develop the confidence, teamwork, leadership and spirit of adventure and exploration of all expedition members.

Twitter: @Brit_exploring

Web: **www.britishexploring.org**

Camps International 18-25

An award-winning expedition specialist that offers life-changing responsible travel experiences throughout Africa, Asia and Latin America. They offer gap year experiences in community and wildlife conservation in Kenya, Tanzania, Borneo, Cambodia and Ecuador. The programmes include four main elements; Community, Wildlife, Environment and Adventure, and the camps are located within communities and wildlife areas, away from the main tourist circuit, enabling all volunteers to become part of the local community and experience complete cultural immersion as a guest, not just a tourist. A two-month experience in Camp Kenya, which includes up to six weeks working in a school or other community project as well as snorkelling, safari and cultural trips, costs from £2,310.

Twitter: @CampsInt

Web: **www.campsinternational.com**

Dragoman Overland 18+

Dragoman has been running adventure trips for over 30 years across the four continents of Africa, Asia, North and South America. The overland tours range from 13 days to 6 months in length. The shorter 2- or 3-week trips offer a snapshot of a country or region; giving travellers a short, sharp adventure travel experience. On the longer tours you could cover a whole continent. For example, join a trans-Africa expedition from Cape Town to Cairo - or in South America, circle the continent.

Twitter: @DragomanTravel

Web: **www.dragoman.com**

Earthwatch 15-18

Earthwatch Teen Expeditions are designed specifically and exclusively for 15 to 18 year olds. Working with projects all around the world, they're hands-on, engaging and meaningful - providing unrivalled opportunities to undertake vital, peer-reviewed scientific field research under the supervision of skilled research teams in a professional setting. Whether you're interested in helping conserve the Amazon Basin's pink river dolphins, snorkel and survey reefs in Belize, or dig for cultural treasures of a Roman villa, Earthwatch has an expedition for you.

Twitter: @earthwatch_org

Web: **www.earthwatch.org**

G Adventures 18+

G Adventures arranges a range of adventure holidays around the world giving you the opportunity to step off the beaten track and experience authentic accommodation and local transportation to bring you face to face with the world's most fascinating cultures, customs and awe-inspiring wildlife. Adventures include a 13-day Cape and Dune experience in Namibia, or Roam Cambodia for a 10-day adventure.

Twitter: @gAdventures

Web: **www.gadventures.com**

GapGuru 17+

GapGuru is a gap year specialist offering a wide range of volunteer, travel and internship opportunities across Asia, Africa, South America & Europe. With GapGuru you could be teaching English in Ecuador, working as a medical intern in India, caring for orphans in Tanzania or trekking up Mount Everest! GapGuru gives you the opportunity to discover new countries and cultures, to meet new people and immerse yourself in local communities. Volunteers work in underprivileged communities, helping those in need, while building their own skills, confidence and experience.

Twitter: @GapYearGuru

Web: **www.gapguru.com**

Gap Year South Africa 18+

Gap Year South Africa works extremely closely with under-resourced local South African communities. South African Gap Year projects contribute to social and economic development and address priority areas such as education, health, moral regeneration and social cohesion. Gap Year South Africa offers 3-week, 5-week, 3-month and 5-month project options in Cape Town, and volunteer projects include Teaching and Education, Sports Coaching, Performing Arts, HIV/AIDS Awareness, Care Work, Medical and Veterinary projects and Environmental Awareness, Scuba Diving, Marine Conservation and Surfing Projects.

Twitter: @GapYear_SA

Web: **http://gapyearsouthafrica.com**

InterRail All ages

Offers information on how to travel around Europe by train including planning your journey, timetables, maps and passes. The most popular product is the Global Pass which gives you flexible train travel in 30 countries.

Twitter: @InterRail

Web: **www.interrail.eu**

Jubilee Sailing Trust 16+

The Jubilee Sailing Trust (JST) is a charity that aims to promote the integration of people of all physical abilities through the challenge and adventure of tall ship sailing. The JST owns and operates two tall ships - LORD NELSON and TENACIOUS - the only two vessels in the world that have been purpose-designed and built to enable a crew of mixed physical abilities to sail side by side on equal terms. If you take on the tall ship challenge with the JST, it could be a short hop around the British coast, a four-week transatlantic challenge, a week's island hopping in the Canary Islands or the Caribbean, or a place in the European Tall Ships' Race

Twitter: @JubileeSailing

Web: **www.jst.org.uk**

Madventurer 17+

As a volunteer, you become part of the Mad Tribe. The spirit of volunteering brings together all shapes and sizes and accents. Each year there is a Mad World Ball in Newcastle upon Tyne, for reunions and reminiscing of the time you've weathered and treasured together. Madventurer rural projects focus on building basic infrastructure to assist local community development. The key focus is youth development and the provision and improvement of health and education through work on schools, clinics, toilets, water storage tanks, community centres and sanitation facilities. Venturers also have the opportunity to teach English and other subjects in local primary schools, as well as getting involved in extracurricular activities such as sports, art and drama.

Twitter: @Madventurer

Web: **www.madventurer.com**

Oasis Overland 17+

Oasis Overland is an adventure travel company with a huge number of overland trips in several continents, including Africa, the Middle East, Latin America, and long journeys across Asia. Oasis Overland trips, mostly in their purpose-built vehicles that can take up to 24 people, vary in length up to 38 weeks. Your expedition could involve anything from 9 days in Egypt to 38 weeks across Africa.

Twitter: @OasisOverland

Web: **www.oasisoverland.co.uk**

The Outward Bound Trust 11 to 24

The Outward Bound Trust run adventure programmes ideal for young people looking to do something different with their summer. They offer a range of one- or three-week experiences, run throughout the summer months, with a range of specialist climbing, biking or paddling adventures. Each programme not only gives you a chance to try out new activities from gorge scrambling to expeditions in the mountains, an Outward Bound experience equips you with new skills and can make a real difference to your CV or university application. Choose from three locations: Loch Eil in the Scottish Highlands, Ullswater in the Lake District or Aberdovey in Snowdonia, Wales.

Twitter: @OutwardBoundUK

Web: **www.outwardbound.org.uk**

Overseas Job Centre — All ages

This site is a guide to living and working abroad, seasonal jobs, working holidays, careers breaks, gap years, volunteer work and long-term round the world travel. It lists volunteer work opportunities around the world from tourism and catering to teaching or working with animals. It gives advice on planning your gap year as well as a useful list of websites for reference and further information.

Twitter: @WorkingTravellr

Web: **www.overseasjobcentre.co.uk**

Quest Overseas — 17+

Specialists in Africa and South America, Quest offer 'Combined Gap Expeditions', in which you can learn a language, work on a community or conservation project and then explore the best of the surrounding countries. This could lead, for example, to Community Development work in Tanzania or a Game Reserve project in Swaziland, together with exploration of southern Africa, or an Animal Sanctuary project in Bolivia, together with exploration of the Andes.

Twitter: @QuestOverseas

Web: **www.questoverseas.com**

Raleigh International 17-24

The Raleigh overseas programme enables participants aged 17 to 24 from all over the world and from all backgrounds to undertake a blend of mental and physical challenges. The full 10-week programme consists of three distinct project phases - sustainable community and environmental projects plus an adventure phase. There are also five-week programmes, which combine your choice of either a community or environmental project with a team-based adventure challenge. Destinations include Costa Rica & Nicaragua, India and Malaysia (Borneo).

Twitter: @Raleigh_

Web: **www.raleighinternational.org**

Royal Geographical Society 16+

Every year the Society supports between 40 and 50 teams of students and researchers to get into the field with a Geographical Fieldwork Grant, the Society's longest-running grant scheme. The three independent travel grants support challenging and inspiring geographical journeys and expeditions and are worth up to £3,000. Full details of the different grants available can be found on the website.

Twitter: @RGS_IBG

Web: **www.rgs.org**

Tall Ships Adventures 16+

The Tall Ships Youth Trust owns a small fleet of six vessels including a tall ship, challenger yachts and a catamaran. They are operated by Tall Ships Adventures and work 12 months of the year both around the UK and abroad, offering sailing holidays. No sailing experience is needed as Voyage Crew are taught everything they need to know.

Web: **http://tallships.org**

The Leap 17+

The Leap offers adventurous team or solo voluntary work placements in Africa, South America and Asia. All placements combine conservation, eco-tourism and community projects, otherwise known as the Three Leaps. This mix of challenges and experiences, combined with adventure travel in the form of scuba diving, kite surfing, white water rafting, riding or polo, should serve to broaden your horizons and surpass your expectations.

Twitter: @GapYearExperts

Web: **www.theleap.co.uk**

Tour Dust 18+

Tourdust is a revolutionary adventure travel agent for independent travellers who are looking to book activity holidays, adventure holidays and tours from expert local operators all around the world. Experiences offered by Tourdust include Inca Trail treks, Galápagos Cruises and trekking in Morocco's Atlas Mountains alongside a host of other unique travel experiences such as Safaris in the Masai Mara and Sea Kayaking in the Aegean.

Twitter: @Tourdust

Web: **www.tourdust.com**

TrekAmerica 18+

TrekAmerica's distinctive style of adventure travel offers something different to your ordinary guided tour. They offer small group adventures across the USA, Canada, Alaska & Central America. Every year thousands of young people from all over the world find that their small group tours offer an easy and dependable way to explore North America.

Twitter: @trekamerica

Web: **www.trekamerica.co.uk**

Trekforce Expeditions 18+

With over 20 years' experience of organising expeditions - that combine real adventure with a serious purpose - in the rainforests, deserts and mountains of the world, Trekforce run one- to five-month expeditions and gap year programmes that tackle tough conservation or development projects, and can be followed by intensive language courses and long-term teaching placements in rural communities. They also offer a series of two- to three-week Extreme Expeditions to the most testing environments around the world, designed to push you to the very limit.

Web: **www.trekforce.org.uk**

VentureCo 17-20

VentureCo's multi-phase travel programmes incorporate development projects, expeditions and adventure travel in Asia, Africa and South America. The ventures are a combination of complementary phases. For example, in South America you would combine a Spanish language phase with a Project phase and an Expedition phase to make one venture. Each phase reveals a different aspect of your host country and together they produce one memorable travel experience. Participation in the venture is the most important element of its success: venturers are team players with considerable input into the everyday running of each phase.

Twitter: @VentureCoUK

Web: **www.ventureco-worldwide.com**

Wind, Sand and Stars 16-23

Wind, Sand and Stars are desert specialists. Working closely with local tribal communities they offer authentic, personal and close-up experiences. The trips have combined desert adventures, mountain treks, camel safaris, field trips, school journeys, silent retreats, pilgrimage to historical religious sites, charity projects and more. Whether travelling through the deserts of Arabia or highlands of Ethiopia they have built strong working relationships with the local people who offer you their warm hospitality and an insight into their traditional ways of life.

Twitter: @Wind_Sand_Stars

Web: **www.windsandstars.co.uk**

Woodlarks Campsite Trust 16+

Situated in twelve acres of beautiful Surrey countryside, Woodlarks Campsite enables children and adults with disabilities to enjoy a host of activities they may never have thought possible. Woodlarks camps can be as tranquil or as adventurous as you want them to be.

Web: **www.woodlarks.org.uk**

Worldwide Experience 17+

Worldwide Experience allows you to work with animals while contributing to global conservation and community programmes. They specialise in conservation projects in Southern Africa but also offer animal rehabilitation projects, veterinary experiences, school groups and game ranger courses. Other activities can include sports coaching and teaching, marine conservation, wildlife photography and filmmaking. All projects are run by specialists in their field who are specifically trained to impart their skills and experience. For example a two-week programme working on a conservation project somewhere in Southern Africa, where you assist in the work of an award-winning conservation team, costs from £709.00 per person.

Twitter: @WorldwideExp

Web: **www.worldwideexperience.com**

Yamnuska Mountain Adventures 17+

Yamnuska Mountain Adventures is a mountain skills and experience organisation. Courses are held by experienced mountain guides and instructors. They specialise in Mountaineering, Rock Climbing, Ice Climbing, Ski Touring, Trekking and Avalanche education at beginner to expert level. Their Three Month Mountain Skills and Leadership Semester based in Alberta, Canada gives participants the skills and experiences for safe mountain travel and leadership. They arrange your accommodation for the whole trip and provide all meals when you are out in the field.

Twitter: @Yamnuska_Mt_Adv

Web: **www.yamnuska.com/climbing-school**

Work Experience

Learn how business works... and get paid for it in some cases! You may be carrying out research, designing prototypes, planning projects, handling customers' needs or devising new working methods. Projects vary depending on company needs.

BBC 14-18+

The British Broadcasting Corporation has work experience placements available in just about every area of BBC activity across the UK. Whatever your age and whichever area you're interested in, there could be something right for you, from advertising, charitable work or entertaining to journalism, music or the World Service. All placements are unpaid and can last anything from a few days to four weeks. Competition is fierce, so before you apply you'll need to consider what you can offer and what you'd like to achieve. Are you good with computers? Have you worked in hospital radio or written articles for your local or college magazine? What do you hope to gain from the placement? What are your ambitions for the future? These are the kind of questions you should be asking yourself.

Web: **www.bbc.co.uk/careers/work-experience**

Gap Medics 16-25

Gap Medics offers the opportunity for those embarking on a career in medicine/nursing to gain valuable and interesting medical work experience in a safe and supported environment. It has provided once-in-a-lifetime medical experiences for over 2,000 students around the world. The cost of the experience varies but includes Hospital work experience placement; Professional supervision & clinical teaching; Safe, sociable accommodation in our own houses; All your food; Airport welcome and transfer; Help with all your preparations; 24/7 support from our expert teams in the UK and overseas.

Twitter: @GapMedics

Web: **www.gapmedics.co.uk**

GlaxoSmithKline 16-18

Leading research-based pharmaceutical and healthcare company, GlaxoSmithKline, offer an annual work experience programme at their research and development sites in Stevenage, Ware and Harlow during the February half term. It is a week packed with interesting experiences. During your week with them, you will learn by doing – on the job – and you will be able to pick up some handy tips from the experienced colleagues around you. Places are available to students in Year 12/13 studying science, IT or engineering. Please note priority is given to students attending schools that are local to the Stevenage, Ware and Harlow areas.

Web: **www.gsk.com/uk/careers/school-students.html**

Pinsent Masons 16-18

International Law firm Pinsent Masons offer a number of work experience placements at their offices in London, Birmingham, Leeds, Manchester, Edinburgh or Glasgow. During your week at the firm you will take part in a business exercise, attend information presentations and seminars in addition to shadowing our lawyers on real issues. You'll also be supervised by one of our trainee solicitors who will help you gain an appreciation of the skills you need to be a good lawyer. These include letter-writing, research, and a good eye for detail.

Web: **www.pinsentmasons.com/en/graduate/our-programmes/school-work-experience**

Year in Industry 17+

The Year in Industry scheme offers paid, degree-relevant work placements in a year out before or during your university course. With opportunities in all branches of science, technology, engineering, maths and business management, you can undertake real projects and learn how business works. The skills you develop should enhance your university education and maximise your graduate job prospects. Many companies view the scheme as an important part of their recruitment programme, and go on to sponsor placement students through university.

Twitter: @TheEDTUK

Web: **www.etrust.org.uk/year_in_industry.cfm**

From typing and temping to word processing or web design, courses listed in this section can both enhance your key skills and improve your future employment prospects. They can increase your effectiveness in higher education making it easier to update research reports and essays.

Brighton Journalist Works 18+

Brighton Journalist Works, in partnership with Brighton's daily newspaper The Argus, offer a 14-week NCTJ Diploma in Journalism. The course trains you for newspapers, magazines and the web, and prepares you for life as a reporter and as a sub-editor. It is a multi-media journalism course which includes researching, reporting and production journalism; it includes video production and shorthand, as well as the essential law and public affairs modules. You are guaranteed three weeks' work experience, and will learn from experienced working journalists in a friendly, professional environment.

Twitter: @journalistworks

Web: **www.journalistworks.co.uk**

News Associates 18+

Based in London and Manchester, News Associates offer NCTJ-accredited courses in Journalism. The 20-week 'Fast Track' course covers reporting, portfolio, shorthand, law, public affairs and either sport or sub-editing. With a packed timetable and 40-hour weeks, it's not for the faint-hearted! News Associates holds free monthly workshops when those interested in journalism training can try simulated news exercises.

Twitter: @NewsAssociates

Web: **http://newsassociates.co.uk**

Oxford Media and Business School 17+

The School's 'Gap Year Life Skills' course is designed to give you an early taste of a university style environment, together with training in key Life Skills such as the use of the latest IT software. The Careers Direct placement bureau will then help you find temping work, which can be invaluable both for later university submissions and for earning cash to fund the rest of your Gap Year.

Web: **www.oxfordbusiness.co.uk**

Pitman Training 17+

There are more than 90 Pitman Training Centres all over the UK, Ireland and the Middle East, training 50,000 people every year. Courses are available in areas such as IT and Business skills, including Bookkeeping and Accounts, Web Design, Shorthand, Spreadsheets and Word Processing.

Twitter: @PitmanTraining

Web: **www.pitman-training.com**

Press Association Training 18+

Press Association Training offer NCTJ-accredited courses in multi-media journalism. The courses are based in London, at the Press Association's headquarters, or in Newcastle in the offices of the publishers of the Evening Chronicle, Journal and Sunday Sun. The 17-week full-time course runs twice a year, in spring and autumn. You'll learn all the basics of being a great reporter and have the chance to produce stories for the Evening Chronicle, The Journal and the Sunday Sun on the Newcastle course, and various London newspapers if you are studying in the capital.

Twitter: @PA_Training

Web: **www.becomeareporter.co.uk**

Quest Business Training 16+

Quest Professional offer practical business skills training to school leavers and university graduates looking to get the skills that employers want and fill in the gaps on their CV. You will develop your practical office IT skills and business communication, as well as increasing your commercial awareness and knowledge of marketing, management, business finance, social and digital media. Throughout the training programmes, you will focus on your future career, CV, job hunting and interview skills technique.

Twitter: @QuestLondon

Web: **www.questcollege.co.uk**

Up To Speed Journalism 18+

Since 2006 Up To Speed have been running courses for aspiring journalists. The courses are designed by professional journalists and photographers and taught by professionals who have worked at the top in British media. Up To Speed journalists have gone on to work in every area of the profession from newspapers to magazines and from broadcasting to online news. Courses are accredited by the National Council for the Training of Journalists (NCTJ) and held in a newspaper building.

Twitter: @Up_To_Speed

Web: **http://uptospeedjournalism.co.uk**

Science, Engineering and Medicine

Many of the opportunities listed here give you the chance to make things happen by taking scientific knowledge and converting it into working products, systems and processes.

ATOM (Advanced Topics on Medicine) Conference 15-18

This is a one-day conference designed to help Years 11, 12 and 13 students who want to hone their UCAS applications for Oxford, Cambridge and all other UK medical schools. It includes the following areas - impartial advice on UK medical schools, mock medical school interviews with feedback, before and after interview techniques, optional DVD of personal interviews and optional UCAS personal statement review.

Web: **www.atomconference.com**

British Science Association 5-19

The British Science Association organises National Science & Engineering Week every March, with over 4,500 scientific, engineering and technology events occurring throughout the country and the Festival of Science in September which includes dialogue events for 14-19 year olds. The Association also runs the nationally recognised CREST awards; project-based award scheme for STEM subjects. Information is sent direct to schools, and more details can be found on the website.

Web: **www.britishscienceassociation.org**

Embryo Veterinary School, Devon 17+

The Embryo team of experienced vets and academics offer a three-day course for aspiring vets, giving detailed analysis of Veterinary Science degree courses, and honest insight into the realities of the job. Set in rural Devon, the course provides an opportunity to spend time in a working veterinary practice environment.

Twitter: @embryovets

Web: **www.embryovets.com**

Engineering Education Scheme 16+

The scheme, sponsored by the Royal Academy of Engineering, aims to help young people achieve their full potential in engineering, science and technology. Students are given the opportunity to work in an engineering environment for a few months before taking A levels.

Web: **www.etrust.org.uk/eese.cfm**

Headstart Courses 16+

A well-established education programme whose aim is to encourage students interested in mathematics, science or engineering to consider technology-based careers. It provides an opportunity for you in Year 12/S5 to spend up to a week at university prior to making your UCAS application.

Web: **www.etrust.org.uk/headstart.cfm**

Medlink 16+

Medlink is a three to five day course for young people considering a career in medicine. It gives delegates the opportunity to listen to and discuss medical school admission and careers in medicine with Deans from a number of medical schools, as well as advice on surviving medical school given by medical students, and gives the chance to talk with practising doctors and medical students. The course is valuable for students in years 12 and 13.

Web: **http://medlink-uk.net**

Medsim 16+

Medsim is a three-day residential course held at the Nottingham University School of Medicine. Medsim offers a rich selection of patient contact and practicals that will considerably strengthen the young person's UCAS application. Most importantly, the experience of working under supervision in small groups, with real patients and equipment, has the benefit of allowing young people to experience what it is like to be a doctor, to deal with patients, to be on-call and work under pressure.

Web: **www.workshop-uk.net/medsim**

Pre-Med Course 16+

Pre-Med Course is a one-day medical careers course run by a team of doctors. The course gives impartial careers information to anyone considering medicine as a career. Topics covered include application procedures, interviews, medical school curriculum, and practical demonstrations.

Web: **www.premed.org.uk**

Royal Institution All ages

An important part of the work of the Royal Institution is to promote an understanding of science in young people. To further this aim, lectures, events and summer schools are held specifically targeted at the new generation of budding scientists.

Twitter: @ri_science

Web: **www.rigb.org**

Salters' Chemistry Camps 14-16

Popular three-day residential Camps for 15-year-olds at universities throughout the UK, packed with exciting chemistry and social events. The aim of the Camps is to encourage young people to participate in the fun of chemistry and motivate them to develop awareness of and a long-term interest in the subject.

Web: **www.salters.co.uk/camps**

Smallpeice Trust 12-17

The Smallpeice Trust is an independent charity that works to encourage more young people to consider a career in Science, Technology, Engineering and Maths. As part of this The Trust offer three- to five-day residential courses to provide students with a real-life insight into various strands of engineering. Students in Years 8-12 are offered the unique opportunity to work with leading engineering companies at top universities around the country in areas such as Biochemical Engineering, Nuclear Engineering and Physics in Engineering.

Twitter: @SmallpeiceTrust

Web: **www.smallpeicetrust.org.uk**

Workshop Conferences 16+

The Workshop offers short residential conferences, covering such career/degree-related topics as: nursing, medicine, physiotherapy, psychology, veterinary science, chemistry, physics, forensics, journalism, dentistry and law.

Web: **www.workshop-uk.net**

Sports Related

Whether you are new to a sport or already experienced, these courses can enhance your performance. Achieving instructor status could provide opportunities to teach a sport to fellow undergraduates and to represent your university in e.g. golf, tennis, sailing, rowing, football.

Alltracks Academy 17+

Alltracks Academy is an ATOL-bonded, family-run company that provides ski & snowboard courses in Canada & France. Courses include early morning powder runs, racing gates, recognised instructor qualifications, avalanche safety training, and backcountry adventures. Held in the world class ski resorts of Whistler and Val d'Isere, their courses range from a couple of weeks to the whole season. They make an ideal way for keen skiers or snowboarders to spend a constructive gap year or career break in the mountains. Alltracks also offer a paid internship working as a ski or snowboard instructor in Whistler, Canada. You complete a 4-week instructor course and are guaranteed a job straight afterwards.

Twitter: @ALLTRACKS

Web: **www.alltracksacademy.com**

Altitude Futures 17+

Based in Verbier, Switzerland, Altitude Futures offers you the chance to become a fully qualified ski or snowboard instructor. Aimed at competent skiers and snowboarders, their 10-week-training gap course provides you with the opportunity to gain a level 1 and 2 BASI (British Association of Snowsport Instructors) ski or snowboard instructor licence, first aid qualification and practical teaching experience whilst skiing or snowboarding at one of the top resorts in the world.

Twitter: @AltitudeVerbier

Web: **www.altitude-futures.com**

Flying Fish 17+

Flying Fish trains and recruits over 1,000 people each year to work as yacht skippers and as sailing, diving, surfing, windsurfing and ski and snowboard instructors. As an experienced yacht skipper or instructor, you can then spend time earning money from your favourite sport. Courses range from two to 22 weeks and are available to complete beginners and for those who already have some experience.

Twitter: @FlyingFishTeam

Web: **www.flyingfishonline.com**

Gap Year Diver 18+

Gap Year Diver specialises in scuba diving trips for people taking time out. All programmes include diver training and are suitable for beginners as well as those with previous experience. Courses include: Learning to dive; Adventure tours and diving; Spanish lessons and scuba diving; Wreck diving tours; Marine Conservation; Underwater filming courses; and Instructor Traineeships. Programmes operate in Egypt, Indonesia, Thailand, Venezuela, Costa Rica, Fiji, The Bahamas, Belize, Honduras and Mozambique.

Twitter: @GapYearDiver

Web: **www.gapyeardiver.com**

International Academy 18+

Become a ski or snowboard instructor on a 5- to 12-week gap year or career break course. Experience world class resorts and gain recognised CSIA, CASI, NZSIA or SBINZ instructor qualifications. Resorts include Banff, Lake Louise, Whistler Blackcomb and Castle Mountain in Canada. Summer courses are also available at Cardrona Alpine Resort in New Zealand. There are also courses in scuba diving, sailing and surfing at some of the most beautiful and challenging waters and locations around the world.

Twitter: @int_academy

Web: **www.international-academy.com**

Jonathan Markson Tennis 10+

A graduate of Christ Church College, Oxford, Jonathan Markson is a former captain and coach of the Oxford University 'blues' tennis team and an international player for Scotland. His company offers tennis holidays and tennis camps in England, Portugal, Spain, Italy, Cyprus, South Africa, Tunisia, Mauritius, Czech Republic, Hungary and the USA. All ages and ability levels are catered for.

Twitter: @JM_Tennis

Web: **www.marksontennis.com**

The Manor House Activity & Development Centre 18+

The Manor House provide a 16-week intensive Outdoor Instructor Training course. During your time on the course you will develop skills in specific activities such as climbing, kayaking, mountain walking, cycling, surfing, beach lifeguard skills, and first aid. You will also work on the theoretical and practical aspects of risk assessments, hazard management, group management and leadership. You will also gain hands-on experience assisting with group activity sessions during the course and be taught the associated soft skills to facilitate your transition to a Professionally Qualified Instructor.

Twitter: @MActivityCentre

Web: **www.manoractivitycentre.co.uk**

NONSTOP Adventure 17+

NONSTOP Adventure is a family-owned company that runs mountain biking, surf, skiing and snowboarding training courses. Whether your passion is for the sea or the mountains, there is a course for you. In most cases courses will result in gaining internationally recognised instructor qualifications that could open up exciting employment opportunities worldwide. All courses are run by the industry's top professionals and focus on general improvement as well as gaining professional instructor qualifications. All abilities welcome. ATOL-protected.

Twitter: @nonstopsnow

Web: **www.nonstopadventure.com**

Peak Leaders 17+

Peak Leaders' Mountain Bike, Surf, Ski and Snowboard courses ensure you will be improving your technical skills, gaining snowsports qualifications, and increasing your understanding of mountain environments, safety and team leading. At the same time, you'll be experiencing life in another culture such as in Canada, New Zealand, South America, France or Switzerland. There are also nine-week summer break, southern hemisphere courses, with the emphasis on travel and adventure.

Twitter: @PeakLeaders

Web: **www.peakleaders.com**

ROCK Sailing 16+

ROCK Sailing offer professional Yachtmaster training in the Mediterranean sunshine of Gibraltar, Spain, Portugal and Morocco. They combine professional training with adventure on courses lasting from 1 to 14 weeks designed to take a complete newcomer to sailing through to being a fully qualified DoT Yachtmaster and Sailing Instructor.

Web: **www.sailinggibraltar.co.uk**

Sporting Opportunities 17+

Sporting Opportunities offer sports coaching volunteer projects which give you the chance to travel to Africa, Asia and South America with likeminded people and volunteer in the community as a sports coach. You will coach sports to children from disadvantaged backgrounds, play sport in the local community and return home with some unforgettable memories. There are a variety of volunteer sports projects to choose from including football, hockey, rugby, netball and many more. You could find yourself coaching football in India, Argentina or Ghana, or perhaps netball and hockey in South Africa.

Twitter: @SportingOpps

Web: **www.sportingopportunities.com**

United Through Sport 18+

United Through Sport is a UK-registered charity that supports sport and recreation projects in Developing World countries. It particularly focuses on four outreach programmes in South Africa, working with the Umzingisi Foundation, to deliver sporting opportunities for over 15,000 disadvantaged children. The sports programmes are run in local communities focusing on rugby, netball, cricket, soccer, hockey, swimming and tennis, and offer the opportunity to volunteer as a sports coach.

Twitter: @utscharity

Web: **www.unitedthroughsport.org**

Language Skills

Learn a new language or simply develop your existing linguistic ability! Effective communication is a vital ingredient in every sphere of human activity.

Bridging The Gap China 18+

Bridging The Gap China offers courses based in the Yunnan province of China that combine Mandarin learning with sightseeing and cultural activities. They provide a unique Mandarin learning experience with emphasis on learning whilst travelling. Consequently, they limit the amount of classroom time and ensure a teacher travels with students everywhere. Not only will you get the chance to practise what you've learnt in real life situations, but you will also visit some of China's most spectacular sights.

Twitter: @BTG_China

Web: **www.bridgingthegapchina.co.uk**

Cactus Language All ages

Cactus Language help over 15,000 people every year learn more than 30 languages, in 60 countries and 500 destinations worldwide. They provide thousands of different courses around the world and can create or tailor any programme specifically to individual needs. Cactus also provide courses for children, under 18s, families and the over 50s. There is the opportunity to learn Spanish in Buenos Aires or Italian in Florence. They also offer TEFL courses for those who wish to teach English abroad.

Twitter: @cactuslanguage

Web: **www.cactuslanguage.com**

CESA Languages Abroad 16+

A Languages for Life course immerses you in a language, teaches you key language skills and provides you with the opportunities to put these skills into daily practice. You will gain a wider and richer knowledge of the vocabulary, grammar and syntax of the language or, at a higher ability level, you can add layers of understanding in the form of nuance and cultural reference critical to real language competence. Students of European languages can see tangible results over an 8- to 16- week period, although you can study for longer. If studying Arabic or Russian, you may need 8 to 20 weeks for serious linguistic improvement, and 12 to 24 weeks for Japanese or Chinese.

Twitter: @CESALanguages

Web: **www.cesalanguages.com**

don Quijote 18+

Travel to Spain or Latin America with don Quijote and learn Spanish at one of their friendly schools. Choose from a wide variety of Spanish courses. You can combine Spanish language lessons with a variety of exciting activities from dance practice to cooking classes. don Quijote schools are a great place to meet new people. As well as an invaluable knowledge of the Spanish language, you will inevitably come away with a new group of friends from all over the world.

Twitter: @don_Quijote

Web: **www.donquijote.co.uk**

ESL - Language Travel 18+

ESL is a specialist in studying languages abroad. They offer courses in more than 20 languages in over 50 countries. With ESL's Gap Year programme, you can learn a language to an excellent standard while fully immersed in a new culture. The programmes last from 3 months and are tailor-made according to your needs and objectives by their experienced language travel consultants. ESL can also arrange voluntary work, internships and paid work in your destination.

Twitter: @esllanguagesuk

Web: **www.esl.co.uk**

Get in2 China 17+

Experience the 'New' Land of Opportunity. Established in 2003, Get in2 China offer the chance to learn Chinese in Beijing or Shanghai. Specialised classes are also available which cover Business Chinese, Chinese Law, News and Current Affairs, and there are courses for both beginners and advanced learners. Paid Internships are also available. In addition they organise trips for sightseeing and other cultural activities to give you the best Chinese experience possible.

Twitter: @Getin2China

Web: **www.getin2china.com**

Language Courses Abroad — All ages

If you are interested in learning Spanish in Spain, studying French in France, doing an Italian course in Italy, German course in Germany, or want to learn Portuguese, Russian, Arabic, Chinese, Japanese or Greek, Language Courses Abroad offer a course and location which could suit your needs and interests. Their language schools are in Europe, Latin America, Asia, Canada and Egypt.

Web: **www.languagesabroad.co.uk**

OISE — All ages

OISE offers intensive language courses in English, French, German and Spanish with either intensive short courses or extended programmes for exam preparation. Students are taught in small groups of 4 or 8 maximum per class at all levels.

The language schools can be found in the UK, France, Germany, Spain, Canada, United States and Australia and are open all year round: during the academic year, during the summer and other vacations.

Twitter: @OISE_Language

Web: **www.oise.com**

Rotary Youth Exchange 15-19

Each year the Rotary Youth Exchange programme sends literally thousands of young people, on long- and short-term exchanges, special interest camps and tours. These aim to promote an insight into another country's way of life, traditions and culture, and to develop lasting friendships.

Web: **www.youthexchange.org.uk**

Spark Spanish 17+

Learn or improve your Spanish with a Spanish Language Course taught in Spain. Spark Spanish runs dynamic Spanish language courses in the city of El Puerto de Santa Maria in Andalusia in southern Spain. Experience the local culture and authentic lifestyle that comes with studying in this historic town. Spark also offer a Demi-pair programme where you can study Spanish at Spark and combine it with the opportunity of living with a welcoming, local family. Spark Spanish are a Cambridge and Trinity certified examination centre.

Twitter: @SparkSpanish

Web: **http://brightsparkspanish.com**

Drama and Music

Opportunities listed here include the chance to work with leading professionals, to develop your individual performing skills and to experience the buzz of live performance.

European Union Youth Orchestra 14-24

The Orchestra is made up of some 120 players, representing all 27 member countries of the European Union (EU). The players are selected each year from over 4,000 candidates aged up to 24, who take part in auditions throughout the EU. Once the members have been selected for the year, you are invited to join the Orchestra to rehearse and perform major works on international stages all over the world. There are two rounds of auditions in the UK and Ireland: Preliminaries are held in Birmingham, Cork, Dublin, Glasgow, London and Manchester; Finals are held in London and Dublin.

Twitter: @EUYOtweets

Web: **www.euyo.org.uk**

National Association of Youth Theatres 14 to adult

The Association supports the development of youth theatre activity through training, advocacy, participation programmes and information services. Its Regional Youth Theatre Festival events include opportunities to perform, take part in a wide range of workshops, see others perform and meet youth theatre members from other areas.

Twitter: @nayttweets

Web: **www.nayt.org.uk**

National Student Drama Festival 16-25

The 2014 Festival will take place in Scarborough. It will feature performances, workshops, discussions, masterclasses and entertainment in venues across Scarborough, including the Stephen Joseph Theatre, University of Hull Scarborough Campus and The Scarborough Spa. The Festival is a seven-day celebration of young people's theatre and will feature the best of British work alongside exceptional productions by young people from across the world. It is for anyone who wants to get involved with drama and the creative industries and is a place where the most inspirational work from diverse, young and emerging artists is celebrated and presented alongside workshops from leading professionals from around the world.

Twitter: @nsdfest

Web: **www.nsdf.org.uk**

National Youth Orchestra of Great Britain 13-19

One of the world's finest youth orchestras, the National Youth Orchestra (NYO) draws together each year 165 talented musicians, aged up to 19, from all over the UK. The orchestra meets during the school holidays at New Year, Easter and Summer for intensive two-week periods of coaching and rehearsal with leading professional musicians and some of the world's finest conductors and soloists, before performing in iconic concert halls such as Symphony Hall, Birmingham, The Sage Gateshead and the Royal Albert Hall.

Twitter: @nyotweets

Web: **www.nyo.org.uk**

National Youth Orchestras of Scotland 8-25

The National Youth Orchestras of Scotland is unique in providing complete orchestral experience for its students aged between 8 and 25, through its comprehensive range of orchestras and training ensembles. NYOS organises training, intensive rehearsals and national and international concert tours. NYOS is committed to introducing musical experiences to all of Scotland's young people.

Twitter: @NYOScotland

Web: **www.nyos.co.uk**

Year Out Drama Company 18+

Year Out Drama provides an exciting, challenging, intensive, practical Drama Course, led by experts in professionally equipped performance spaces. This is a full-time programme providing an intensive practical drama course with a theatre company feel. The course includes Acting, Directing, Design, Costume, Voice Work, Movement, Text Study, Theatre Trips and at least four full-scale performances during the year, including a production at the Edinburgh Festival.

Web: **www.yearoutdrama.com**

Art and Design

Whether marvelling at masterpieces of the Renaissance or producing your own portfolio of design ideas, you can use a gap year to develop new insights into the world of art and design.

Art History Abroad 16+

The aim of AHA's courses is to enjoy Italy, see a wealth of beautiful art while having fun. The six-week Gap year course involves travelling throughout Italy to study at first hand many masterpieces of Italian art. Depending on the course you choose, you will stay in Venice, Florence, Rome, Naples, Siena, Perugia, Palermo, Syracuse or Verona. Your course may make day visits to Padua, Ravenna, Vicenza, Pisa, Arezzo, Pompei, Tivoli and Assisi. There are also summer holiday courses of two or four weeks in July and August.

Twitter: @AHAcourses

Web: **www.arthistoryabroad.com**

Central Saint Martins College of Arts & Design 16-18

Take a short course in art and design at one of Britain's most revered art institutions. The courses are available over weekends, or during the Easter, Summer and Christmas holidays. Subjects include Fashion and Textiles, Fine Art, Graphic Design, Interdisciplinary, Media Arts, Theatre and Performance, Three Dimensional Design. Fundamental to study at the College are experimentation, innovation, risk-taking, questioning and discovery, within a highly supportive learning environment, no matter which discipline you choose to study.

Twitter: @csmevents

Web: **www.csm.arts.ac.uk/shortcourses**

John Hall Venice 16+

A nine-week pre-university introduction to some of the most thought-provoking achievements in the Western world, from the classical past to today. A week in London introduces themes which are developed in Venice (6 weeks). Optionally this is followed by a week in Florence and a week in Rome. The course is conducted through on-site visits and a series of lectures by a team of world-class experts; it includes not only art, but also music, world cinema and literature. There are also practical classes offered in studio life drawing and portraiture, photography, cookery and Italian language.

Twitter: @johnhallvenice

Web: **www.johnhallvenice.com**

KLC School of Design 18+

The one-week Introduction to Interior Decoration at the KLC Studio in Chelsea gives an insight into the whole process of interior design. The approach is practical with a combination of lectures and workshops that demonstrate how to plan a room layout and how to create a cohesive interior style by developing ideas from a basic concept. Also popular is the one-week Introduction to Garden Design.

Twitter: @KLCSchool

Web: **www.klc.co.uk**

Cookery Skills

Some of the courses listed here could help you decide whether you would like to train for a career as a professional cook; others can lead to gap year employment as a chalet cook; others are specifically geared to help future university students prepare simple meals for survival on something more than beans on toast after leaving home.

The Avenue Cookery School, London 16+

The Avenue Cookery School offer a variety of courses from basic to advanced, including 'The Really Useful Course', a five-day course for undergraduates and Gap Year students covering cooking and 'really useful' information. The relaxed and friendly atmosphere at The Avenue can turn even the most nervous beginner into a confident 'foodie'.

Twitter: @AVENUECOOKERY

Web: **http://theavenuecookeryschool.com**

Ballymaloe Cookery School, Ireland 16+

Run by Ireland's most famous TV cook Darina Allen, Ballymaloe offers a highly regarded 12-week certificate course, graduates of which are in demand all over the world. There is also a wide range of shorter courses - some suitable for complete beginners, others aimed at more experienced cooks. A special time every day is lunch, when teachers and students sit down together to enjoy a three-course meal, which the students have prepared using recipes from the demonstrations.

Twitter: @Ballymaloe

Web: **www.cookingisfun.ie**

Cookery at the Grange, Somerset 17+

Cookery at the Grange has a worldwide reputation for its Essential Cookery Course. The Grange was the first cookery school to offer the four-week residential course when it started in 1981, so for thirty years has built up a reputation as second to none for its success in helping students with their careers and lives.

Web: **www.cookeryatthegrange.co.uk**

Edinburgh School of Food and Wine 16+

Among a wide range of courses, you may be particularly interested in the Edinburgh School's four-week intensive certificate course, designed to help you earn your keep during a gap year. This practical course will give you the fundamental skills needed to cook for, say, a ski chalet or a highland lodge, and a grounding in cookery for life. Also highly relevant is the one-week 'survival course', designed to develop your culinary talents through a combination of demonstration and practical sessions. Their Six Month Diploma is their flagship course, it is popular with school leavers, looking to learn about the culinary world, also with the opportunity of job prospects at the end of the course.

Twitter: @ESFW

Web: **www.esfw.com**

Le Cordon Bleu 18+

Le Cordon Bleu is a world-renowned network of educational institutions dedicated to providing the highest level of culinary and hospitality instruction through world class programmes. You might try the four-week 'Essentials Course' at the institute's London School, or you could consider a short course at one of its centres in France, Canada, Japan, Australia, Mexico or South Korea.

Twitter: @lcbeurope

Web: **www.cordonbleu.edu**

Leiths School of Food and Wine, London 17+

The School offers a varied menu of courses for professional cooks and enthusiastic amateurs. Especially relevant for readers of this book is the one-week 'Absolute Beginners' cooking course. This is aimed at those leaving home or cooking on their own for the first time and wishing to equip themselves with basic skills and recipes to allow them to cook nutritionally balanced food on a budget. The course also looks at how to make very simple dishes look impressive, and at how humble ingredients can make delicious meals.

Twitter: @Leithscookery

Web: **www.leiths.com**

Nick Nairn Cook School, Scotland 16+

TV chef Nick Nairn is the man behind the Nick Nairn Cook School, a foodie haven built around a single objective: teaching kitchen confidence. The cook school offers a variety of courses, mostly one day, where visitors can pick up new skills, inspiration and knowledge all whilst preparing their own gourmet lunch. The school is hidden away in the foothills of the Trossachs, right at the heart of some of Scotland's finest scenery, yet less than an hour away from Edinburgh or Glasgow.

Twitter: @thecookschool

Web: **www.nicknairncookschool.com**

Orchards Cookery, Worcestershire 16+

The one- and two-week 'Chalet Cooks' courses can show you how to master the art of being a great chalet cook, enabling you to get the most out of a gap year job in the mountains. The school also offers a recruitment service helping students with CV writing, interview training etc. Alternatively, the five-day 'Off to University' course covers healthy, delicious and affordable meals for students, including easy entertaining.

Twitter: @OrchardsCookery

Web: **www.orchardscookery.co.uk**

Padstow Seafood School, Cornwall 16+

TV chef Rick Stein's famous cooking school mostly caters for adults, but does offer half-day courses for students during the Easter and summer holidays. For both those who've never cooked with fish and seafood enthusiasts alike, the half-day course teaches you the techniques you'll need in order to create really impressive fish dishes

Twitter: @TheSeafood

Web: **www.rickstein.com**

Tante Marie School of Cookery, Surrey 16+

Renowned for its professional Diploma courses, Tante Marie offers three shorter courses particularly suited to readers of this book. Whether you are keen to go for a gap year job in a stunning location, would like to take your culinary skills to a higher level or just want a short introduction to cooking well for yourself, family and friends, there could be a suitable course for you. The one-term 'Cordon Bleu Certificate' is highly valued by ski companies and other gap year employers, although you might also consider the four-week 'Essential Skills' course. If you simply want to eat well at university, look at the one- or two-week 'Beginners' courses, offering an introduction to good food and healthy eating.

Twitter: @TanteMarie

Web: **www.tantemarie.co.uk**

We mention at several points in this publication that it will cost you a fairly considerable sum - often several thousand pounds - to participate in some of the projects listed. This is particularly true of many of the international community, environmental or scientific projects.

For example, to go overseas with Project Trust in 2013, you will be expected to raise £5,000, including a deposit of £250. Project Trust will raise another £500 approximately on your behalf to subsidise the full costs of your year abroad.

Organisations such as Project Trust receive no government assistance and all funds must be raised either by project managers or by volunteers like you.

Given that the aim of this book is to provide you with ideas to help develop your personal, learning and thinking skills, we believe that raising sponsorship can be an important part of this process. It shows others your determination and initiative, and it will help you establish in your own mind just how well you can respond to a challenge. You will have to start by learning how to fundraise and how to make the most of the support available.

Experienced organisers of such projects say that most volunteers are surprised by the response to their efforts and many not only hit their target but actually raise more than the sum required. Only a small number each year have problems and even they can usually be helped to find suitable sponsors.

Should you decide to opt for a project with a sizeable participation fee, you will find that the organisers will normally send you, once accepted, a comprehensive pack containing fundraising ideas and information. In addition, there should be an experienced member of staff able to give you help and advice by email or over the telephone.

The list below should give you a clear idea of the level of fundraising support you should look for when researching a possible project:

- **Advice on fundraising:** Does the selection process introduce the idea of fundraising through a seminar or workshop, encouraging you to think about it constructively?
- **Ongoing support:** What mechanism exists for you to keep the organisers informed of your progress? If you are struggling, do they provide practical advice?
- **Fundraising meetings:** Will you be invited to one or more fundraising meetings, where you can get together with fellow volunteers to share ideas and experiences?
- **Bulletin board:** Is there a website bulletin board allowing you and your fellow volunteers to keep in touch?

Fundraising ideas

The best starting point is always to look inside yourself! There should be no need to turn your life around completely to raise the required funds. Consider what you are already good at and love doing, then think about how you can use your skills to make the money you will need.

If you are good at music, for example, you could try your hand at busking, performing at various events or offering home tuition.

If your interests are more sporting, you could arrange a tournament where teams pay to enter and you provide the service of organising it and setting up suitable prizes.

If you can cook, you could offer a catering service for dinner parties and other social gatherings.

If you are green-fingered, you could offer a gardening service or bring on seeds and cuttings to sell at every opportunity.

If none of these applies, you could simply get a part-time job of any sort and start saving regularly to establish your fund.

Once you have a service to offer, goods to sell or a job to find, turn first to your immediate circle of family, friends and school, college or other social contacts, perhaps in a youth or sports club. If they can't offer you direct support, ask them to think about who they could put you in touch with, or who they might be prepared to approach on your behalf. Before long, you should have a long list of potential customers/employers/sponsors!

While you are raising money, don't forget that you will have other things to buy. You might, for example, need a top quality sleeping bag or rucksack, both of which are likely to be expensive. Baggage insurance is another important extra.

When you go, you will need to take some spending money with you: perhaps around £1,000 for a year-long project, although this can depend upon which country you go to. Even if you can afford it, you shouldn't think of taking so much money overseas that you might be tempted to live and travel in a way that would not sit easily with your role as a volunteer.

Managing Risk

Many of the suggestions in this book contain an element of risk. That is part of their attraction...and you will no doubt see little point in trekking through a jungle or across a mountain range if you are going to be as cosy and safe all the time as you are in an armchair at home. Nevertheless, we could not possibly encourage you to take unnecessary risks and we recommend that you venture overseas only with a reputable organisation with experienced leaders and stringent operating procedures designed to avoid foolhardy misadventure.

We cover a broad range of health and safety issues in our brief quiz on page 99 and we would ask you to spend some time reading this section and visiting the recommended websites. Amongst them, the

Know before you go site managed by the Foreign and Commonwealth Office is absolutely essential (see page 104).

In addition, we suggest that you use the checklist below when choosing an organisation with which to undertake your trip. This will help to ensure that you are in safe hands and will be travelling responsibly.

- **Crisis Management:** Is there a comprehensive crisis management policy in place? How robust is it and how are staff trained to implement it?
- **UK Support:** Does the organisation maintain a 24-hour emergency telephone line for family and friends in the UK?
- **Insurance:** Does the organisation have a comprehensive company insurance policy with a specialist provider?
- **Leaders:** What is the organisation's recruitment policy in relation to the experience and qualifications of expedition leaders? What knowledge do they have of the countries they work in? Do they have relevant language and first aid skills? Does the Criminal Records Bureau carry out checks of their backgrounds?
- **Risk Assessment:** Do expedition leaders undertake daily monitoring of activities in order to maintain the safety of participants? Are written risk assessments available for consultation? Are participants encouraged to carry out their own risk assessments during an expedition?
- **In-Country Support:** Do leaders have up-to-date contact lists for medical and logistical support in the country you will be visiting?
- **Participant Preparation:** What level of pre-departure training and/or in-country orientation is provided for participants?
- **Equipment:** How often is equipment reviewed and replaced? Is safety equipment provided as standard? Do leaders carry comprehensive first aid kits?
- **Transport:** How do leaders assess in-country transport? Is there a policy regarding the use of public or private transport options? Is road transport undertaken at night?

- **Responsible Travel:** What is the organisation's policy in relation to monitoring and minimising the long-term impact of expeditions such as the one you are considering? Is there a long-term commitment to cultural sensitivity and sustainable development?
- **Financial Transparency:** Can the organisation demonstrate that your financial contributions are spent directly on the project and nowhere else?
- **Feedback:** Is there evidence that feedback from participants and staff is assessed and acted upon where necessary to improve future provision?

A final word. While we have tried our best, as publishers of this book, to ensure that you understand the nature of potential hazards overseas - how to recognise and overcome them - we must stress that you cannot rely totally on us or even on the very best provider of specialist gap year activities. You must use your own common sense and initiative to help you to spend your time as safely as possible.

Finding a Focus

When you have researched the ideas in this book, photocopy these pages and complete a worksheet for each project that interests you. Our 10-point plan will help you focus on finding the right programme to develop your personal learning and thinking skills.

Name of organisation
Type of activity
1. **What is it that appeals to me?** *(Gaining relevant experience, travel, helping others, earning money)*
2. **Am I eligible?** *(Right age, available at the right time, suitable qualifications)*
3. **What exactly will I be doing?** *(Working with others, undertaking/learning about research methods, cookery)*
4. How will I benefit from this programme?
5. How will other people benefit from my involvement?

6. How much will it cost? *(Total budget, raising funds, putting down a deposit)*
7. Who will I be signing up with? *(Commercial company, registered charity)*
8. What do I need to arrange? *(Travel, insurance, health check, vaccinations)*
9. Is there any pre-programme training or briefing?
10. What happens afterwards? *(Debriefing, maintain contact with organisations/ providers, inform future participants, obtain certificate recording my achievements)*

Am I Ready for a Trip Abroad?

If you are planning to travel abroad as part of your personal development, try our brief quiz to see how well prepared you are!

1. INSURANCE ISSUES
   - (a) I will investigate a range of different types of insurance to cover my travel and placement/project ☐
   - (b) I will take out travel insurance for the journeys to and from my placement/project ☐
   - (c) I guess that I'm on our family annual travel insurance and that my parents' insurance policies will cover all eventualities ☐
2. THE COUNTRY I INTEND TO VISIT
   - (a) I have researched the laws and customs of my planned destination as well as the usual food, currency and weather type research ☐
   - (b) I have looked at holiday websites to find out about the country I intend to visit ☐
   - (c) I'll pick up everything I need to know just by being in the country for several months ☐
3. VISAS AND PERMITS
   - (a) I have checked out the necessary visas and work permits for the country I intend to visit ☐
   - (b) I will see if I need a visa ☐
   - (c) Someone will sort out whatever has to happen about a visa for me ☐
4. HEALTH
   - (a) I will check with my local surgery to see if I need any special injections or healthcare for the country I am visiting a couple of months before the departure date ☐
   - (b) I will ask my mum to take a look on the internet to see if there is anything I need to do about health care arrangements for my visit ☐
   - (c) I won't bother to do anything special about healthcare as I am young and healthy ☐
5. SAFETY
   - (a) I have seriously considered a number of ways of ensuring my safety when I am on my placement and I have discussed safety plans with my family ☐
   - (b) I am always careful about my well being and I won't need to do anything extra for my placement ☐
   - (c) I have no safety worries and I can look after myself ☐

How did you do?

If you answered (a) to all the questions then you have made a good start. All (b) then you have a bit more work to do. All (c) then you really must do a lot more research.

Points to consider

1. Insurance issues

It'll never happen to me!

It can happen to you; things can go wrong. You could fall ill or have an accident; you could have money or luggage stolen; your visit might be cancelled or cut short through injury or illness; your family may need to fly out to be with you if there is a serious incident. So take out insurance. Make sure it's comprehensive and covers you for medical and repatriation costs as well as any dangerous sports or activities.

If you get injured or ill as a result of drugs or alcohol, your insurance may be invalidated and your travel operator can refuse to fly you home.

2. The country I intend to visit

You must read up on the laws and customs of your chosen destination, to avoid offending people or breaking local laws, however unwittingly. The best starting point for this is the Foreign and Commonwealth Office, with its 'Know before you go' awareness campaign aimed at encouraging British travellers to prepare better before going overseas. Visit the website at: **www.gov.uk/knowbeforeyougo**, follow them on twitter **@FCOtravel** or phone 0845 850 2829.

If you are contemplating taking drugs whilst on holiday abroad or bringing some back with you, stop and think - otherwise your trip of a lifetime could end up lasting a lifetime in jail! Bear in mind that: 2,528 British nationals were detained overseas during 2005, a third of them for drugs-related offences; many countries outside the UK refuse to grant bail before trial and may detain people in solitary confinement; you will still get a criminal record in the UK if arrested with drugs abroad; if you've been caught with drugs abroad, you're unlikely ever to be allowed to visit that country again.

3. Passports, Visas and Work Permits

If you wish to travel abroad you must hold a full ten-year passport, even for a day trip. Apply in good time. In the UK, you can get advice from the HM Passport Office website at **www.gov.uk/hm-passport-office** or call them on the Passport Advice Line on 0300 222 0000 (open 8am to 8pm Mon-Fri and 9am to 5.30pm weekends & public holidays). Some countries have an immigration requirement for a passport to remain valid for a minimum period (usually at least six months) beyond the date of entry to the country. Therefore, if appropriate, ensure your passport is in good condition and valid for at least six months at the date of your return. This is a requirement of the country concerned, not the UK Passport Service, and any questions should be addressed to their Consulate or Embassy.

Outside the UK, you should get advice in an emergency from the nearest British Embassy, High Commission or Consulate. Staff can issue standard replacement passports in most places, and all missions are able to issue emergency passports if more appropriate.

If you plan to travel outside British territories, you may require a visa to enter the country you are going to. Check visa requirements with your project organiser or travel agent or contact the Consulate or Embassy of the country you plan to visit.

If you plan to work outside the European Union, you will need to obtain a valid work permit before you go.

Some Passport Tips:

- Make a note of your passport number, date and place of issue (or take a photocopy), and keep separately in a safe place.
- Check your passport expiry date.
- Write the full details of your next of kin in your passport.
- Leave a photocopy with a friend or relative at home.
- Take a second means of photo-identification with you.
- Keep your passport in the hotel safe and carry a photocopy with you.
- If your passport is lost or stolen overseas, contact the nearest British Embassy, High Commission or Consulate immediately for advice.

4. Health

- Check the Department of Health website at: **www.nhs.uk/Healthcareabroad** for general medical advice for travellers.
- Check what vaccinations you need with your GP at least six weeks before you travel.
- Check if your medication is legal in the country that you are visiting.
- Pack all medication in your hand luggage.
- If you are taking prescribed medication, take the prescription and a doctor's letter with you.
- If you are travelling within the European Economic Area or Switzerland, you should get a free European Health Insurance Card (EHIC) by visiting the Department of Health website as above. You can also obtain the EHIC by completing the Department of Health leaflet 'Health Advice for Travellers' (HAFT), available through most UK Post Offices or by telephoning 0845 606 2030. The EHIC entitles you to free or reduced-cost medical care but you will still need medical and travel insurance.
- Be safe in the sun. Avoid excessive sunbathing, especially between 11am and 3pm, and wear a high factor sunscreen.
- Drink plenty of water. If you drink alcohol or use some kinds of drugs your body can become dehydrated, especially in a hot climate.
- Find out the local emergency number and the address of the nearest hospital when you arrive overseas. Your rep, local guide or project manager should know.

5. Safety

Be aware of what is going on around you and keep away from situations that make you feel uncomfortable. Avoid potentially dangerous 'no-go' areas, in particular after dark. Use your common sense and make sure you are constantly assessing and reassessing your personal safety. Be aware of drugs - these have been used in incidents of rape, so keep your wits about you.

Keep an eye on your possessions. Never leave your luggage unattended or with someone you don't completely trust. Be aware of pickpockets, who tend to operate in crowded areas, and lock up your luggage with padlocks. Make sure you have copies of all important documents such as your passport, tickets, insurance policy, itinerary and contact details. Keep these separate from the originals and leave copies with your family and friends.

Work out how much money you'll need on a daily basis and work to a realistic budget. Be sure to take enough money, as the Foreign and Commonwealth Office can't send you home free of charge if you run out!

Finally, tell friends and family your plans before you go and keep in regular contact, especially if you change your plans. Consider taking a roam-enabled mobile and use text or email to keep in contact. Don't promise too much - promising to call home every day is unrealistic and will only cause your family and friends to worry when you don't!

Best Gap Year

This site will provide you with worldwide gap year jobs, courses and travel opportunities, from winter jobs in a ski resort or summer sports teaching courses in Australia to medical projects in China. It offers a huge range of ideas across the world with opportunities to take part in conservation and community projects, teaching, and sports and volunteering. It also provides valuable advice on gap year planning, health and other issues.

Web: **www.bestgapyear.co.uk**

Foreign & Commonwealth Office Website

The Foreign and Commonwealth Office website offers lots of advice for anyone thinking of embarking on gap year travel. From top tips on insurance and money to advice on staying healthy and getting the right visa, you will find all you need to know to plan the safest and most enjoyable gap year travel.

Phone: 0845 850 2829

Twitter: @fcotravel

Web: **www.gov.uk/gap-year-foreign-travel-advice**
www.gov.uk/knowbeforeyougo

Gap Advice

Gapadvice.org was founded in 2005 to provide an independent source of impartial advice and information for people of all ages looking to take a gap week, month or year. It provides advice for young people after leaving school, for undergraduates and those who have just graduated as well as those looking for career breaks. It contains information on considering your gap year, investigating it, organising it, doing it etc., all covered in a comprehensive five step plan.

Web: **www.gapadvice.org**

Gapyear.com

Gapyear.com is a social media and travel advice website created by backpackers, for backpackers, devoted to giving you everything you could possibly need when planning or taking a gap year. It hosts and supports a community that is passionate about real travel and ready to share experience and advice. The community is backed up with expert guides.

Twitter: @gapyeardotcom

Web: **www.gapyear.com**

Hostelling International

Youth hostels can provide you with reliable, reasonably priced accommodation in many parts of the world. Hostelling International is the brand name of more than 90 Youth Hostel Associations in 90 countries, operating 4,000 plus hostels. Unlike bland motels, impersonal hotels or dodgy backpacker rooms, youth hostels are usually fun, lively meeting places, full of like-minded people.

Twitter: @Hostelling

Web: **www.hihostels.com**

InterHealth

InterHealth specialises in providing detailed and specific travel health advice tailored to remote and exotic destinations. Its website includes a section for gap year travellers. The online shop can supply everything from first aid kits to mosquito nets and water purification tablets.

Twitter: @InterHealth

Web: **www.interhealth.org.uk**

Objective Travel Safety

Your school or college may be willing to organise a safety and security awareness training course to help you prepare for a gap year. One organisation specialising in this type of work is Objective Travel Safety.

Twitter: @ObjectiveTravel

Web: **www.objectivegapyear.com**

STA Travel

Specialists in cheap flights, adventure trips and travel deals for young people, STA Travel have several pages of gap year travel tips on their website.

Twitter: @STATravel_UK

Web: **www.statravel.co.uk**

World Travel Guide

Want a heads up on what the visa regulations are for visitors to India, how much duty free you can bring back from France, what the main sights are in Yemen or when the best time of year to go to Jamaica is? It's all available here, and quickly searchable by country or region.

Twitter: @WTGTravelGuide

Web: **www.worldtravelguide.net**

Suggested Reading List

Gap Years - The Essential Guide
- Emma Jayne Jones, Need2Know, 2012

Backpacking: The ultimate guide to first time around the world travel
- Michael Huxley, CreateSpace Independent Publishing Platform, 2013

The Gap-year Guidebook 2013: Everything You Need to Know About Taking a Gap-year or Year Out
- Alex Sharratt, John Catt Educational Ltd, 2012

Your Gap Year: The Most Comprehensive Guide to an Exciting and Fulfilling Gap Year
- Susan Griffith, Crimson Publishing, 2012

The Rough Guide to First-Time Around The World
- Doug Lansky, Rough Guides, 2013

Work Your Way Around the World
- Susan Griffith, Vacation Work, 2011

Lonely Planet's Best Ever Travel Tips
- Tom Hall, Lonely Planet Publications, 2010

The Backpacker's Bible
- Suzanne King, Portico, 2010

The Travellers Good Health Guide
- Dr Ted Lankester, Sheldon Press, 2006

Volunteer: A Traveller's Guide to Making a Difference Around the World
- Lonely Planet Publications, 2013

Green Volunteers 8th Edition: The World Guide to Voluntary Work in Nature Conservation
- Fabio Ausenda, Green Volunteers, 2011

Archaeo-Volunteers: The World Guide to Archaeological and Heritage Volunteering
- Fabio Ausenda, Vacation Work, 2009

Easter Revision Courses

The following independent colleges offer specific retake and intensive revision courses, giving you the opportunity to improve your performance in a wide range of subjects during the Easter vacation.

Abbey Colleges

The Abbey Colleges are part of the Alpha Plus Group - formerly Davies, Laing and Dick Education Group - which currently comprises twenty independent schools, colleges and sixth form colleges. Abbey Colleges in Birmingham, Cambridge, London and Manchester offer intensive retake courses for GCSE and AS and A Level.

Web: **www.abbeycolleges.co.uk**

Ashbourne Independent Sixth Form College, London

Easter revision courses seek to motivate students to strive for the highest grades at A level and GCSE, and to develop independence and self-reliance. As a private college, Ashbourne is able to offer classes which average five students per group.

Twitter: @AshbourneLondon

Web: **www.ashbournecollege.co.uk**

Collingham College, Kensington, London

Intensive tuition in small classes enables individual needs to be met. Groups are Board-specific as appropriate and are formed according to syllabus, topics, texts and so on. The courses are planned to give a clear understanding of the essentials of the syllabus and to teach exam techniques, so that you can use your knowledge to best effect.

Web: **www.collingham.co.uk**

Duff Miller Sixth Form College, South Kensington, London

Duff Miller offers Easter Revision courses across a wide range of A Level and GCSE subjects. They act to inspire, motivate and fulfil academic potential. The primary emphasis of the revision courses is to enhance subject knowledge and establish a rigorous, disciplined and effective approach, resulting in peak exam performance.

Web: **www.duffmiller.com**

Harrogate Tutorial College

Easter Revision courses at Harrogate are designed to help students achieve examination grades well above those they originally expected, but are not intended for students who have done little or no work in their subjects. The small classes - average four, maximum eight students - generate an informal, student-centred approach with the emphasis on high quality work.

Web: **www.htcuk.org**

Justin Craig Education

Established in 1981 and with more than 20 centres around the country, Justin Craig Education provides GCSE, AS and A2 group revision courses. Offering small, informal tutorial groups taught by friendly, enthusiastic and experienced tutors, Justin Craig Education has helped over 100,000 students achieve the grades needed to get into their chosen universities. Tel: 0845 06 06 555.

Web: **www.justincraig.ac.uk**

Lansdowne College, London

Lansdowne College has run Easter Revision courses for over 20 years, helping students to realise their full academic potential at both GCSE and A Level, and enabling them to progress onto their chosen path for their studies. Students are often unaware of exactly what examiners are looking for and subsequently unsure of what makes an A grade answer. The Easter Revision courses remedy this by focusing not just on the subject content, but also on extensive and comprehensive examination preparation, including a mock examination at the end of the course.

Web: **www.lansdownecollege.com**

Mander Portman Woodward (MPW)

MPW is an independent sixth-form college group, with colleges in London, Birmingham and Cambridge. In addition to full-time GCSE courses, AS courses and A2 courses over a very wide range of subjects and with no restrictions on subject combinations, MPW offers intensive A level and GCSE retake courses and revision courses over Easter. Characterising all courses is an absolute maximum of eight students within any one class and a strong emphasis on exam technique and exam practice.

Web: **www.mpw.co.uk**

Millfield School, Somerset

On its Easter Revision course, Millfield offers specialist tuition at GCSE, AS and A2 level, in a broad range of subjects to small groups of students, providing a balance of taught content and rehearsal of technique. Students from all schools are welcome. Courses are offered on both a residential and non-residential basis.

Web: **www.millfieldenterprises.com**

Oxford Tutorial College

Oxford Tutorial College organises short intensive revision courses at Easter and supplementary teaching to support the work being done at school. OTC also offers tailor-made first-time and retake A Level courses. There is a mixture of individual tuition and small group seminars.

Web: **www.otc.ac.uk**

Rochester Independent College, Kent

Intensive Easter revision courses at Rochester provide an opportunity to gain an overview of the syllabus and a chance to practise applying knowledge to real examination questions. This helps with recall of facts and hones skills required for accurate question interpretation and structuring full and concise answers. Most importantly, the courses give a real confidence boost at a crucial time.

Twitter: @RICollege

Web: **www.rochester-college.org**

Taster Courses

Taster Courses

Almost all universities and colleges organise pre-application Open Days, giving you an opportunity to visit the campus, meet some of the staff and students, and attend a short talk on a subject in which you are interested. Details of these days can be found in the *Open Days* booklet published by UCAS.

We focus here on courses that some universities and colleges provide to give you a more detailed opportunity to experience academic and social life on campus. Please note that we refer to *Taster Courses* for the sake of clarity but universities are independent institutions and don't always use the same terminology. It is, therefore, not unusual to find *Taster Courses* described as Summer Schools or Academies (at any time of year!), Campus Days or Find Out More Days.

Duration

Course lengths vary: some are one-day courses only, others may last a weekend or even a week. Most courses are free (although you will normally have to pay for travel and accommodation). You may have the chance to stay overnight on campus.

Format

Most *Taster Courses* include lectures, discussions and tutorial sessions, so that you can meet the departmental staff and get hands-on experience using the facilities. This can provide an important insight into how the university or college operates. ***Taster Courses*** should also allow you to find out about other aspects of undergraduate life, such as sporting, musical, drama and cultural activities, accommodation and other amenities.

Benefits of Attending a Taster Course

- You are more likely to choose a higher education course to suit your interests and abilities and to avoid an unsuitable one.
- You can highlight your attendance in the personal statement section of your UCAS application.
- You may find that a course or campus is not for you, and decide to reject it in favour of others.
- You can discuss your impressions with admissions tutors at universities or colleges during interviews.

Science and Technology tasters

In addition to the Taster Courses listed on the following pages, see pages 58 to 62 for details of the science and technology tasters, particularly those organised by Headstart and the Smallpeice Trust.

University of Aberdeen Summer School for Access

The Summer School is a ten-week, full-time programme of study, which runs from June to August each year. You have to undertake four courses and complete coursework and exams, on successful completion of which (at minimum Grade 12 out of 20) you will be guaranteed a place on an undergraduate programme at the University of Aberdeen. You may also use the Summer School for entry into other universities across the UK, although you must contact the other institutions and agree their entry requirements before you start.

If you are a student from within the European Union, you are not normally required to pay tuition fees for the Summer School and free accommodation may also be available, based on household income and expenditure.

For further details email: **SSA-Aberdeen@abdn.ac.uk** or visit the website: **www.abdn.ac.uk/lifelonglearning/ssa**

Aberystwyth Summer University

The Summer University provides a free six-week, full-time, residential (or non-residential) programme for young people from Community First areas in Wales, those receiving ALG, or other non-traditional backgrounds. The programme consists of Core Skills together with academic modules (including Art, Business Studies, Biological Sciences, Childhood Studies, Computing and IT, Countryside Management, Creative Writing (in English), English Literature, European Languages, Film and Media Studies, Environmental Studies and Geography, History, International Politics, Law, Mathematics, Physics, Psychology, Sports and Exercise Science - subject to numbers). All students who successfully complete the Summer University are offered a guaranteed progression route to an appropriate degree scheme at Aberystwyth University, subject to conditions and a reduced offer.

Application forms available from mid-November 2013 for Summer 2014. For further details contact: **wpsi@aber.ac.uk**

Aberystwyth University

The Schools and Colleges Liaison Team can arrange on-campus taster days and workshops for school and college groups with an opportunity to stay overnight in a hall of residence. Please email **marketing@aber.ac.uk** if you would like to discuss the day/residential programmes available at the University.

Aston University, Birmingham

Aston organises a range of Masterclasses and Sixth Form Conferences providing a taster of university life in specific subject areas including Biology, Business, Chemistry, English Language, Engineering, Law, Mathematics, Modern Foreign Languages (French, German and Spanish), Optometry, Pharmacy, Psychology, Politics and Sociology.

For further information please contact Angela Morris at **morrisa@aston.ac.uk**; telephone: 0121 204 4787; website: **www.aston.ac.uk/schliaison**

University of Birmingham School of Engineering

There may be some opportunities to experience engineering by attending one-day taster courses in the five Schools of Engineering during the spring/summer. For full details visit the website at **www.birmingham.ac.uk**.

University College, Birmingham

University College offers a Summer School in various subjects. Full time - 3 days/2 nights. Limited spaces only. Also Master Classes offered in a choice of 9 subjects on one morning or afternoon. Limited spaces only.

For further details on their summer school and master classes, please contact Ruth Walton, telephone: 0121 232 4042, email: **ruthwalton@ucb.ac.uk**, or visit the website: **www.ucb.ac.uk**

Bradford College

The college offers a variety of taster days for courses in both further and higher education. To attend or request more information about taster days, contact the Education Liaison Team Leader, telephone 01274 433084 or email:
educationliaison@bradfordcollege.ac.uk

University of Chichester

Several departments at the University of Chichester run taster days, in which you can sample lectures or participate in workshops. In some cases, these events are open to all prospective applicants, while others invite people who have already applied, to help them make their final choice. You can book online for taster days - usually held in March/April - in the following areas: Business and IT Management, Humanities, Arts, Sport Science and Sports Studies, Education and Teaching, and Social Sciences.

Further information can be found at: **www.chi.ac.uk/tasterdays**

Cornwall College, Newquay

Offers university course taster days on various dates between October and June. These taster days give prospective students the opportunity to look around the campus and its facilities, talk to programme lecturers and discover more about the course of interest. Students can also find out about tuition fees and the financial support available, meet current students and discover more about student life in Cornwall. Booking is essential. For further details, please telephone 01637 857 957 or visit the website at: **www.cornwall.ac.uk**

University of Exeter, Penryn Campus Open Days

A University of Exeter, Penryn Campus Open Day is packed with opportunities for you to find out if the University of Exeter is right for you. As a visitor to our small and friendly campus, near Falmouth, you can spend a day attending sample lectures, discussing programme options with our leading academics and finding out from current students what it's really like to study at a top research-led university in a beautiful location. There are also tours of the campus and facilities, including our on- and off-site accommodation, student bar and sports centre. Prospective Geology and Mining Engineering students can visit our test mine. At the Penryn Campus programmes include Biosciences, English, Environmental Science, Flexible Combined Honours, Geography, Geology, History, Mathematics and the Environment, Mining Engineering, and Politics and Renewable Energy.

For full details, visit the website at: **www.exeter.ac.uk/visit**

University of Exeter, College of Engineering, Mathematics and Physical Sciences

The Pre-University Physics Course is offered in June/July. For further details please contact **pupc@exeter.ac.uk** or visit the website at: **www.exeter.ac.uk/pupc**

Glyndwr University

Glyndwr University hosts a number of open days and interactive sessions each year which could help you if you have not yet made the decision to enter HE. The focus is on demystifying HE, increasing awareness of the opportunities available, answering questions about finance and support, building confidence and skills, and getting to know the campus and facilities.

For further details visit the website at: **www.glyndwr.ac.uk**

University of Leeds

Leeds has an international reputation for its teaching and research. We offer a range of courses and opportunities to help you develop into an articulate, highly-skilled and confident graduate ready to pursue the career of your choice. Find out more about Leeds and what they offer at the website, **www.leeds.ac.uk**, and visit one of their open days. If you make Leeds one of your five choices you may be invited for a detailed departmental visit.

Register for open days at: **www.leeds.ac.uk/opendays** or email **opendays@leeds.ac.uk**

London University Taster Course Programme

With over 160 courses in 70 different subject areas at numerous university institutions, the Taster Course Programme provides the opportunity to experience life as a university student in the subject area of your choice, ranging from medicine and dentistry to drama and film studies. The taster courses run from half a day to one week, and are usually available between March and July. All courses are non-residential and provided free of charge. You may apply for up to three courses via the online application form. The Careers Group, University of London administers the programme and in 2013 the following colleges participated. (Visit the website at **www.london.ac.uk/tasters** or email: **tastercourses@london.ac.uk** for an up-to-date list of participating colleges in 2014.):

Birkbeck:

Arts and Humanities
Criminology & Criminal Justice
English Literature
Film
History of Art
Journalism
Languages and Culture
(French, German, Japanese, Portuguese, Spanish)
Law
Management and Organizational Psychology
Media
Philosophy
Psychology
Theatre Studies

BPP University College:

- Accounting
- Banking & Finance
- Business
- Law

City University, London:

- Accounting and Finance
- Aeronautical Engineering
- Automotive & Mechanical Engineering
- Bio-Medical Engineering
- Business Studies & Management
- Civil Engineering
- Computing
- Economics
- Electrical, Electronic and Computer Engineering
- Film, music, and the arts: Creative industries
- International Politics
- Investment and Financial Risk Management; Banking and Finance
- Journalism
- Law
- Midwifery
- Music
- Nursing
- Optometry
- Psychology
- Radiography
- Sociology
- Speech and Language Therapy

Courtauld Institute of Art:

- History of Art

Goldsmiths:

- Computing
- Design
- English
- History
- History of Art
- Management
- Media & Communications, Journalism
- Music Computing
- Politics
- Psychology
- Sociology

Heythrop College:

Abrahamic Faiths
Philosophy
Philosophy, Religion & Ethics
Theology

Imperial College:

Computing
Maths and Computing

King's College:

Biomedical Engineering
Chemistry
Classics
English and Comparative Literature
English Language & Communication
European Studies and European Politics
French
Geography
German
Global Health & Social Medicine
Informatics
Language, Literature and Culture of the Hispanic and Lusophone Worlds
Liberal Arts
Maths
Midwifery
Nursing
Nutrition
Philosophy
Physics
Science Engagement & Communication
Theology and Religious Studies

London Metropolitan:

Art & Design
Business
Criminology and Sociology
Early Years Teaching, Early Childhood Studies and Education Studies
English, Journalism and Media
Health, Social Care, Youth and Community Work
Law
Politics, Governance & International Relations

London School of Economics & Political Science (LSE):

Anthropology
Geography & Environment
International History
Law
Philosophy
Sociology

London South Bank University:

Engineering Product Design
Product Design

Queen Mary, University of London:

Astrophysics
Business and Management Studies
Dentistry
Economics
Electronics and Computing
Environmental Science
Geography
Mathematics
Maths with Business and Finance
Physics
Pure Mathematics

Royal Holloway:

Biosciences
Classical World
Comparative Literature and Culture
Computer Science
English
French
German
Geography
History
Italian
Mathematics
Media Arts
Music
Philosophy
Physics
Politics
Psychology
Spanish

Royal Veterinary College:

Bioveterinary Sciences
Veterinary Medicine
Veterinary Nursing

School of Oriental & African Studies (SOAS):

Arts and Humanities
Languages and Cultures
Law
Social Science

St George's Hospital:

Medicine

The Careers Group:

Careers in Law
Careers in Medicine
Career Options for Science, Technology, Engineering and Maths

UCL:

Anthropology
Arts and Sciences
Classics and Ancient World Studies
Construction
East European Languages
Electronic and Electrical Engineering
Engineering
English
Medical Physics
Science and Religion
Science and Technology Studies
Women in Engineering
Women in Mathematics
Women in Technology

University of East London:

Architecture, Computing and Engineering
Psychology

University of Greenwich:

Computing
Film and TV Production
Games and Digital Media
Mathematics

University of London Institute in Paris:
French

University of West London:
Aviation and Tourism Management

University of Westminster:
Biology

Loughborough University

Engineering Experience - Loughborough's Schools of Engineering have been running this highly successful two-day event for the last 24 years. Engineering Experience takes place once a year. Open to year 12 (lower sixth form) students, the event gives an insight into engineering at university. During their stay at the University, students have the opportunity to visit a number of engineering departments including Aeronautical and Automotive Engineering, Mechanical and Manufacturing Engineering, Electronic and Electrical Engineering, Chemical Engineering and Materials), learn about different engineering options, talk to lecturers and tutors about engineering courses and experience student accommodation, the Students' Union and catering. Spaces are limited.

For further information visit the website at: **www.engexp.info** or email: **engexp@lboro.ac.uk**

Newcastle College

Taster courses are offered in Art and Design, Beauty and Complementary Therapies; Business Management and Computing; Construction and Civil Engineering; Engineering and Science; Health Care and Public Services; Music, Media and Performing Arts; Sport and Exercise; Travel, Aviation and Hospitality. Taster courses are usually run during school holidays.

For further details visit the website at: **www.ncl-coll.ac.uk**; telephone: 0191 200 4000 or email: **enquiries@ncl-coll.ac.uk**

Newcastle University

Newcastle University holds a number of Visit Days each year, which are an excellent opportunity to see the University at its bustling best and discover more about the subjects you're interested in. To find out about the Visit Days and other opportunities to get a feel for student life at Newcastle visit the website:
www.ncl.ac.uk/undergraduate/visit

University of Reading Food and Nutritional Sciences Summer School

Are you a young scientist with an interest in a career in food? The Department of Food and Nutritional Sciences at Reading offers an annual short introductory course in late June/early July for lower 6th form students (Year 12). The course is sponsored by manufacturing and retail companies in the food industry.

For further information, email: **food@reading.ac.uk** or visit the website: **www.reading.ac.uk/food**

Royal Agricultural University

The RAU's Land-Based Careers Taster Course is a two-day residential short course and is aimed at 16-19-year-olds (although mature students may also find it of interest). It gives an insight into the career opportunities that exist in the food and land-based industries, both in the UK and worldwide. It also provides an opportunity to learn more about the courses on offer at the College.

For full details and a downloadable application form, visit the website at: **www.rau.ac.uk** or email: **jenny.maguire@rau.ac.uk**

Shrewsbury College of Arts and Technology

Secondary school pupils from around Shropshire are invited to 'taster sessions' at Shrewsbury College to give them an insight into life in Further Education. The College has three campuses, at London Road, Radbrook and Telford. Tasters at London Road will include Accounting, Art & Design, Business, Catering, Computing & IT, Performing Arts, Public Services, Sports Studies and Travel & Tourism. Also at London Road will be tasters run by the Technology Faculty, including Brickwork, Carpentry & Joinery, Painting & Decorating, Electrical Installation, Plumbing, Engineering and Motor Vehicle. At Radbrook campus, pupils can sample Childcare, Hair & Beauty and Health & Social Care. At their Telford Construction Centre tasters are available in Plastering, Brickwork and Painting & Decorating.

For further details visit the website at: **www.shrewsbury.ac.uk** or telephone 01743 342332.

University of Southampton

The University of Southampton will be hosting open days for prospective students and their parents in July and September. The programme of events includes both general and subject-specific presentations and drop-in points as well as tours of academic schools, campuses and halls of residence. Advance booking is highly recommended.

For further information, please visit:
www.southampton.ac.uk/visit

Sparsholt College Hampshire

If you are considering a career in the land, environment or animal industries, Sparsholt College Hampshire offers a number of taster days. Subjects include Agriculture, Animal Management, Arboriculture and Forestry, Equine, Fishery Studies, Gamekeeping and Conservation, Horticulture, Land-based Engineering, Sport and Public Services. These special programmes can be valuable in helping to make course and career choices.

Full details are available from **www.sparsholt.ac.uk** or can be obtained by emailing: **courses@sparsholt.ac.uk**

Sutton Trust Summer School

Sutton Trust Summer Schools offer an opportunity to try University life for over 1,700 young people every year. The programme consists of lectures, seminars and tutorials but also various social activities. The programme runs at Bristol, Cambridge, Edinburgh, Nottingham, St Andrews, Durham, Imperial College London and UCL.

The Sutton Trust Summer Schools are open to all students in Year 12 at maintained schools or colleges in the UK. Places are limited. Priority will be given to students:

- whose family background has no history of higher education
- whose parents are in non-professional occupations
- who have achieved at least 5 A/A*s at GCSE
- Please visit the website for full eligibility criteria

Courses are available in areas including: English, History of Art, Theology, Drama, Languages, History, Philosophy, Sciences, Computer Science, Maths, Social Sciences, Economics, Politics, Law, Engineering, Medicine, Dentistry and Veterinary Science.

The Sutton Trust meets all costs incurred by the student including travel, food and accommodation. For full details, visit the website: **www.suttontrust.com**

Swansea University

Taster courses are available in various subject areas and have previously included Psychology, Engineering and Science as detailed below. Visit the website **www.swansea.ac.uk** for full details.

Engineering Summer School is open to any Year 12 student who is considering applying for an Engineering degree. There is a small cost to include all food, accommodation and activities. You can register your interest by emailing **engineering@swansea.ac.uk**

Headstart Cymru Engineering Summer School is for students living or studying in Wales. It is similar to the format above but run in partnership with EESW Stem Cymru and subsidised places are available. For further information and an application form visit the Headstart Cymru website. Applicants must apply directly through EESW Stem Cymru.

Psychology afternoons are usually held in February. Prospective students can meet academic staff and attend an introductory talk and various taster talks. Places must be booked in advance via **psychology.admissions@swansea.ac.uk**. For further details contact Karen Huxtable – telephone 01792 513023.

At the Science Summer School students can experience a series of taster days in Swansea's five College of Science departments carrying out experiments and workshops in bioscience, computing, geography, maths and physics. Contact **ross.davies@swansea.ac.uk**.

Warwickshire College

Warwickshire College open events are offered at their centres in Leamington, Rugby, Moreton Morrell, Warwick and Henley-in-Arden in Warwickshire and Pershore in Worcestershire. The college also offers taster days in land-based subjects such as equine, agriculture, countryside, horticulture, animal welfare and veterinary nursing at Moreton Morrell and Pershore. These taster events provide an opportunity to experience what it's like to be a student at Warwickshire College - they cover practical hands-on sessions and lecture samples in a friendly environment and in a great countryside location.

For further details of general open events and taster days available, visit the website at: **www.warwickshire.ac.uk/events**

University of the West of Scotland

A Summer School is offered at the Dumfries Campus in business and computing. It gives the opportunity to try out new subjects, experience university life, enhance your qualifications, develop study skills, boost confidence and improve your employability. Apply online at: **www.uws.ac.uk/study-at-uws/summer-schools**

Introductory level study is also available in other subjects at campuses in Ayr, Dumfries, Hamilton and Paisley, e.g. First Steps to Nursing, First Steps to University, First Steps in IT and Career Planning. These modules are delivered on a part-time basis starting in September, January and June each year. For details telephone 0800 027 1000 or visit the website: **www.uws.ac.uk**

The University of York subject taster days are aimed at students in Year 12, who would like an insight into degree-level study before applying to university. Their taster days allow visitors to hear about multiple related academic disciplines on one day, and subject conferences which focus on just one academic discipline.

For students who are not sure about what they want to study, or whether university is the right option, taster days are the perfect opportunity to find out more.

For full details, visit the website: **www.york.ac.uk/tasterdays** or contact the student recruitment team by phone: 01904 323196; email: **admissions-liaison@york.ac.uk**

Indexes

Subject Index

Activity Instructors 23, 37
Adventure Travel 38-40, 43, 45, 47-48, 50
Animal Care 23-24
Animal Sanctuary 44
Art & Design 81-82
Art History 81-82
Au Pair 9
Beach Lifeguard Skills 67
Business Skills 54-57
Camp Counsellor 8, 10, 11
Care Work 41
Chemistry 61-62
Climbing 43, 67
Community Development 7, 9, 15, 17, 19-20, 23, 25, 27-29, 31, 38, 42, 44-46, 50
Conservation Projects 7 11-14, 16, 23, 24, 26-27, 32-33, 38, 44, 46, 48, 50
Cookery Skills 84-88
Cycling 67
Dentistry 62
Desert Specialists 49
Design 82
Drama 77-79
Drama Festival 78
Eco-tourism 12, 46
Engineering 59-60, 62
Environmental Conservation 19, 26, 41, 45
Farming Placements 11, 13
Foreign & Commonwealth Office Website 104
Forensics 62
Forest Conservation 9
Forest Expedition 12
Heritage Camp 32
HIV/AIDS Awareness 8, 16, 25, 41
Horse Riding 46
Hostelling 105
Ice Climbing 50
Internships 15, 24, 27-28
Journalism 16, 24, 51, 54-57, 62
Kite Surfing 46
Language Skills 19, 25, 48, 71-75
Law 53, 62
Marine Conservation 10, 12, 16, 41, 50, 65
Maths 60, 62
Media 55
Medicine 8, 11, 16, 24, 40-41, 52, 58, 60-62
Mental Health 29
Mountain Bike 43, 67-68
Mountaineering 50
Music 77-79
Nannying 37
National Trust 33
Nursing 52, 62
Orchestra 77-79
Orphanage Placements 8, 11, 16, 21, 28, 40
Outdoor Instructor Training 67
Overland Expedition 39, 43
Performing Arts 41
Physics 62
Physiotherapy 21, 62
Polo 46
Psychology 62
Revision Courses 110-113
Rock Climbing 50
Royal Geographical Society 45
Safari 38, 47, 49
Sailing 42, 46, 65-66
Science 59-62
Scientific Field Research 38-39
Scuba Diving 41, 46, 65-66
Sea Kayaking 47
Skiing 14, 23, 37, 50, 64-68
Snorkelling 38
Snowboarding 64-68
Sports Coaching 7-8, 11, 25, 41, 50, 69
Sports Programmes 69
Surfing 41, 65-68
Tall Ships 42, 46
Teaching English 13, 21, 22, 24, 28, 40, 42
Teaching Placement 7-8, 10-11, 13, 15-16, 18, 48
TEFL 18
Technology 62
Tennis 66

Underwater Filming 65
Veterinary 41, 59, 62
Water Sports 23, 37
Web Design 56
White Water Rafting 46
Wildlife Photography 50
Work Experience 51-53
Working Holiday 15, 19, 20, 23, 27, 37, 44
Working with Children 13, 15, 22-23, 29, 31
Working with Disabilities 19, 31, 49
Work with Animals 50
Working with the Elderly 19, 29, 31
Yacht Skippers 65, 68
Year in Industry 53
Zoo Work 11

Please note: this index relates primarily to activities mentioned in our brief descriptions of opportunity providers on pages 5 to 113. We cannot guarantee to have covered every activity offered by every provider.

Geographical Index

Albania 13, 21, 26
Argentina 11, 13, 15, 20, 26, 71
Australia 10-11, 15-16, 18-20, 22, 26-27, 37, 74
Bahamas 16, 65
Belize 10, 16, 23, 65
Bolivia 24
Borneo 16
Botswana 7, 16, 18, 24
Brazil 11, 13, 15, 18, 22, 26
Bulgaria 26
Burma 22
Cambodia 12, 15-16, 18, 19, 21-24, 26
Cameroon 21, 26
Canada 10, 13, 15, 20, 22, 47, 50, 64, 66, 68, 74
Chile 13, 22, 24
China 7, 10-11, 13, 15-16, 18-21, 24, 26, 71, 73-74
Costa Rica 15, 17-18, 21-22, 45, 65
Cyprus 15, 66
Czech Republic 66
Dominican Republic 24
Dubai 11
Ecuador 7, 13, 15-16, 18, 20-22, 26
Egypt 65, 74
Eire 13, 84
Estonia 26
Ethiopia 15, 21, 49
Fiji 16, 17, 20, 65
France 13, 20, 22-23, 26, 64, 68, 74
Galápagos Islands 16, 21-22
Germany 11, 13, 26, 74
Ghana 8, 10-11, 13, 15-16, 20-21, 23-24, 26
Gibraltar 68
Greece 15, 17, 74
Guatemala 13, 15, 16
Guyana 24
Honduras 11, 21, 24, 65
Hong Kong 24
Hungary 66
Iceland 26
India 7, 11, 15-18, 20-22, 24-26, 28, 45
Indonesia 18, 65
Israel 20
Italy 13, 26, 66, 71, 74, 81-82
Jamaica 24
Japan 13, 20, 24, 26, 74
Jordan 22
Kenya 7-8, 11, 15, 17-18, 21-22, 26
Korea 13
Latin America 12, 24, 38, 43, 72, 74
Laos 17, 22
Lesotho 26
Madagascar 9-11
Malawi 7, 20-21, 24
Malaysia 18, 24, 26, 45
Malta 13
Mauritius 7, 26, 66
Mexico 7, 13, 16-17, 21
Moldova 21
Mongolia 21
Montserrat 12
Morocco 13, 21, 26, 68
Mozambique 18, 65
Myanmar 22
Namibia 16, 18, 24
Nepal 7, 10, 15-18, 21-23, 25-26
New Zealand 10-11, 13, 15, 19-20, 22, 26, 66, 68
Nicaragua 45
Nigeria 13
Palestine 21
Panama 15
Peru 15-18, 21-24, 26
Philippines 12, 15
Poland 20
Portugal 15, 26, 66, 68, 74
Romania 11, 16, 22, 26
Russia 21, 74
Rwanda 15
Senegal 21, 24
Seychelles 17
Sierra Leone 25
Singapore 19
Slovakia 26
South Africa 7-8, 10-11, 13, 15-18, 20-26, 41, 66, 69
Spain 13, 15, 17, 23, 26, 66, 68, 72, 74-75
Sri Lanka 18, 21, 24, 26
Swaziland 18, 24, 44
Switzerland 64, 68

Tanzania 7-8, 11, 16, 18, 21-22, 25
Thailand 7, 11, 15, 17-19, 21-24, 26, 65
Tibet 22
Tunisia 66
Turkey 13
Uganda 7, 11, 15, 21, 24, 25
UK 13, 15, 23, 25-26, 31, 32-35, 46, 49, 66-67, 74
Ukraine 21
USA 8-11, 13, 15, 17, 19, 25-26, 29, 47, 66, 74
Vanuatu 20
Venezuela 65
Vietnam 15, 18, 20-23
Worldwide 12-14, 17, 19, 24-25, 27-29, 38-40, 47-48, 50, 71
Zambia 16, 21-22, 25-26
Zimbabwe 7, 16, 25-26

Please note: this index relates primarily to countries mentioned in our brief descriptions of opportunity providers on pages 5 to 88. We cannot guarantee to have covered every country offered by every provider.

Index of Taster Course Subjects

Abrahamic Faiths 124
Accounting 123, 129
Aeronautical Engineering 123, 127
Agriculture 128-129, 131
Animal Management 129
Animal Welfare 131
Anthropology 125-126
Arboriculture and Forestry 129
Architecture 126
Art 118
Art & Design 124, 127, 129
Arts 120
Arts and Humanities 122, 126
Arts and Sciences 126
Astrophysics 125
Automotive Engineering 123, 127
Aviation and Tourism Management 127
Banking & Finance 123
Beauty Therapy 127
Biological Sciences 118
Biology 119, 127
Biomedical Engineering 123-124
Biosciences 121, 125, 131
Bioveterinary Sciences 126
Building Skills 129
Business Studies 118-119, 123-124, 129, 131
Business and IT Management 120
Business Management 125, 127
Career Options for Science, Technology, Engineering and Maths 126
Careers in Law 126
Careers in Medicine 126
Catering 129
Chemical Engineering 127
Chemistry 119, 124
Childcare 129
Childhood Studies 118, 124
Civil Engineering 123, 127
Classics 124-126
Comparative Literature and Culture 125
Complementary Therapies 127
Computer Engineering 123
Computing 118, 123-127, 129-131
Construction 126-127
Countryside Management 118, 131
Creative Writing 118
Criminology and Sociology 124
Criminology & Criminal Justice 122
Dentistry 125, 130
Design 123
Drama 130
East European Languages 126
Economics 123, 125, 130
Education and Teaching 120, 124
Electrical Engineering 123, 126-127
Electronic Engineering 123, 126-127
Electronics and Computing 125
Engineering and Sciences 119, 124, 126-127, 130
Engineering Product Design 125
English 121, 123-126, 130
English and Comparative Literature 124
English Literature 118, 122
Environmental Science 121, 125
Environmental Studies and Geography 118
Equine Studies 129, 131
European Languages 118
European Studies and European Politics 124
Film 122-123
Film and Media Studies 118
Film and TV Production 126
Fishery Studies 129
Food Science 128
French 119, 122, 124-125, 127
Gamekeeping and Conservation 129
Games and Digital Media 126
Geography 121, 124-125, 131
Geology 121
German 119, 122, 124-125
Global Health & Social Medicine 124
Hair & Beauty 129
Health & Social Care 124, 127, 129
History 118, 121, 123, 125, 130
History of Art 122-123, 130
Horticulture 129, 131
Humanities 120
Informatics 124

International History 125
International Politics 118, 123
International Relations 124
Investment and Financial Risk Management 123
Italian 125
Japanese 122
Journalism 122-124
Land-based Engineering 129
Languages and Cultures 122, 124, 126, 130
Law 118-119, 122-126, 130
Liberal Arts 124
Management 123
Management and Organizational Psychology 122
Manufacturing Engineering 127
Mathematics and the Environment 121
Maths 118-119, 124-126, 130-131
Maths and Computing 124
Maths with Business and Finance 125
Mechanical Engineering 123, 127
Media 122-125, 127
Medical Physics 126
Medicine 126, 130
Midwifery 123-124
Mining Engineering 121
Music 123, 125, 127
Music Computing 123
Nursing 123-124
Nutrition 124, 128
Optometry 119, 123
Performing Arts 127, 129
Pharmacy 119
Philosophy 122, 124-125, 130
Philosophy, Religion & Ethics 124
Physics 118, 121, 124-125, 131
Plumbing 129
Politics 119, 123-125, 130
Politics and Renewable Energy 121
Portuguese 122
Product Design 125
Psychology 118-119, 122-123, 125-126, 131
Public Services 127, 129
Pure Mathematics 125
Radiography 123
Science and Religion 126
Science and Technology Studies 126
Science Engagement & Communication 124
Social Sciences 120, 126, 130
Sociology 119, 123, 125
Spanish 119, 122, 125
Speech and Language Therapy 123
Sport Studies 129
Sport and Exercise 118, 120, 127
Theatre Studies 122
Theology 124, 130
Travel & Tourism 127, 129
Veterinary Medicine 126
Veterinary Nursing 126, 131
Veterinary Science 130
Women in Engineering 126
Women in Mathematics 126
Women in Technology 126

Please note that some institutions do not list specific subjects for taster courses. We therefore suggest that you study pages 116 to 132 to see if a campus you would like to visit is included.

Use the COA taster courses website to select courses which suit your preferred dates and locations. Visit: **www.coa.co.uk/opendays**

Organisation Index

Abbey Colleges 110
Adventure Jobs 37
Africa and Asia Venture 7
African Conservation Experience 7
Agape Volunteers 8
Alltracks Academy 64
Altitude Futures 64
Americamp 8
Art History Abroad 81
Ashbourne Independent Sixth Form College 111
ATOM (Advanced Topics on Medicine) Conference 58
Au Pair in America 9
Australia Working Holiday 37
Azafady 9
Ballymaloe Cookery School 84
BBC 51
Best Gap Year 104
Blue Ventures 10
Bridging The Gap China 71
Brighton Journalist Works 54
British Exploring 38
British Science Association 59
BUNAC 10
Cactus Language 71
Camp America 11
Camps International 38
Central Saint Martins College of Arts & Design 81
CESA Languages Abroad 72
Changing Worlds 11
Collingham College 111
Community Service Volunteers 31
Concordia 12
Cookery at the Grange 85
Coral Cay Conservation 12
CSV Heritage Camps 32
Do-it 32
don Quijote 72
Dragoman Overland 39
Duff Miller Sixth Form College 111
Earthwatch 39
Ecoteer 13
Edinburgh School of Food and Wine 85
Embryo Veterinary School 59
Engineering Education Scheme 59
ESL - Language Travel 73
European Union Youth Orchestra 77
Experiment in International Living 13
Flying Fish 65
Foreign & Commonwealth Office Website 104
Frontier 14
G Adventures 40
Gap Advice 104
GapGuru 40
Gap Medics 52
Gapwork 14
Gapyear.com 105
Gap Year Diver 65
Gap Year South Africa 41
Get in2 China 73
GlaxoSmithKline 52
Global Choices 15
Global Volunteer Network 15
Global Volunteer Projects 16
Greenforce 16
GVI Foundations 17
Habitat for Humanity 17
Harrogate Tutorial College 111
Headstart Courses 60
Help to Educate 18
Hostelling International 105
InterHealth 105
International Academy 66
International Voluntary Service 19
InterRail 41
IST Plus 19
i to i Volunteering 18
John Hall Venice 82
Jonathan Markson Tennis 66
Jubilee Sailing Trust 42
Justin Craig Education 112
Kibbutz Volunteers 20
KLC School of Design 82
Language Courses Abroad 74
Lansdowne College 112
Lattitude Global Volunteering 20
Le Cordon Bleu 86
Leiths School of Food and Wine 86
Love Volunteers 21

Madventurer 42
Mander Portman Woodward 112
Medlink 60
Medsim 60
Millfield School 113
National Association of Youth Theatres 77
National Student Drama Festival 78
National Trust 33
National Trust for Scotland 33
National Youth Orchestra of Great Britain 78
National Youth Orchestras of Scotland 79
News Associates 55
Nick Nairn Cook School 87
NONSTOP Adventure 67
Oasis Overland 43
Objective Travel Safety 106
OISE 74
Orchards Cookery 87
Outreach International 21
Overseas Job Centre 44
Oxford Media and Business School 55
Oxford Tutorial College 113
Oyster Worldwide 22
Pacific Discovery 22
Padstow Seafood School 88
Peak Leaders 68
PGL 23
Pinsent Masons 53
Pitman Training 56
PoD Volunteer 23
Pre-Med Course 61
Press Association Training 56
Prince's Trust Volunteers 34
Projects Abroad 24
Project Trust 24
Quest Business Training 57
Quest Overseas 44
Raleigh International 45
Reach 34
Real Gap Experience 25
Restless Development 25
Rochester Independent College 113
ROCK Sailing 68
Rotary Youth Exchange 75
Royal Geographical Society 45
Royal Institution 61
Salters' Chemistry Camps 61
Smallpeice Trust 62
Spark Spanish 75
Sporting Opportunities 69
STA Travel 106
Tall Ships Adventures 46
Tante Marie School of Cookery 88
The Avenue Cookery School 84
The Conservation Volunteers 26
The Leap 46
The Manor House Activity & Development Centre 67
The Outward Bound Trust 43
Tour Dust 47
Travellers Worldwide 26
TrekAmerica 47
Trekforce Expeditions 48
Twin Work And Volunteer 27
United Through Sport 69
Up To Speed Journalism 57
VentureCo 48
vInspired 35
Visit Oz 27
Volunteer Action for Peace 28
Volunteering England 35
Volunteering India 28
VSO 29
Winant Clayton Volunteers 29
Wind, Sand and Stars 49
Woodlarks Campsite Trust 49
Workshop Conferences 62
World Travel Guide 106
Worldwide Experience 50
Worldwide Volunteering 30
Yamnuska Mountain Adventures 50
Year in Industry 53
Year Out Drama Company 79
Year Out Group 30